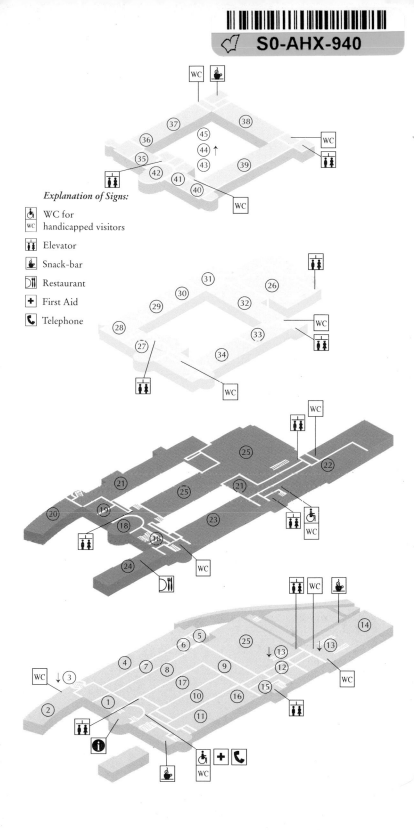

S0-AHX-940

Explanation of Signs:

- WC for handicapped visitors
- Elevator
- Snack-bar
- Restaurant
- First Aid
- Telephone

Guide to the Museum

Deutsches Museum

This brief guide is designed to help you find your way around the Deutsches Museum. The ground floor and basement are described on pages 8 to 59, the first floor on pages 60 to 89, and the second floor on pages 90 to 115. The third floor and the floors above it are described from page 116 onwards. Occasionally we have to depart from this order, as some departments, such as Aeronautics, extend over several floors or may be entered from a different floor, as is the case with Astronautics. The descriptions of these departments are found in the guide according to the easiest points of access.

The various floors of the museum are dedicated to the following main topics:

Ground Floor and Basement:
Engineering & Technology, Land Transport, Marine Transport

First Floor:
Physics and Chemistry, Music, Aeronautics & Astronautics

Second Floor:
Crafts & Trades

Third Floor and above:
High Technology, Agriculture, Astronomy

The collections of the Deutsches Museum cover many more fields of knowledge and there are over 40 departments in all. Areas of special interest are all listed in the index to this guide.

It may be worth your while to seek out some of the quieter sections of the museum. On the one hand, they are good places to take a breather, on the other you may well make some interesting discoveries as there are plenty of attractions here too.

Along with the permanent exhibitions, the Deutsches Museum also holds special exhibitions in some of the rooms. The museum staff will be happy to provide information and directions. Posters in the stairways give details of current special exhibitions. You are also welcome to attend the film shows, lectures, and demonstrations (some basic knowledge of English is necessary). The relevant dates and rooms are given on page 6.

A technical museum is never really complete. One collection or another is always being added to or brought up to date and it may just happen that the section which particularly interests you is closed when you come. We trust you understand that this is in the long-term interest of all our visitors.

We hope you will have an enjoyable and informative visit and that you will also find time to relax among the Deutsches Museum's numerous masterworks of science and technology.

Time	Floor	Demonstration in the museum (15–20 min.)
9.45	G	Mining *(60 min.)*
10.00	G	Machine tools
	1	Aeronautics
	1	Energy Technologies
	6	Zeiss-Planetarium *(Tickets at Information Desk)*
10.30	G	Locomotives
	G	Aeronautics
	G	Marine Navigation
	G	Moulding and casting of metals
	2	Hand-made paper
	2	Glassblowing
	3	Observatory *(West dome, open till 11.30)*
11.00	G	High-Voltage plant
	1	Chemical experiments *(Mon. to Fri.)*
	2	Astronautics
	2	Glassblowing
	4	Amateur radio *(60 min.)*
11.30	G	Locomotives
	G	Power Machinery
	1	Plastics (Industrial Chemistry)
	3	Agriculture and food technology
12.00	6	Zeiss-Planetarium *(Tickets at Information Desk)*
12.45	B	Motor vehicles
13.00	G	Locomotives
	1	Optics (Physics)
13.45	G	Mining *(60 min.)*
14.00	G	High-Voltage plant
	1	Aeronautics
	1	Musical Instruments
	1	Energy Technologies
	2	Glassblowing
	3	Agriculture and food technology
	6	Zeiss-Planetarium *(Tickets at Information Desk)*
14.30	G	Aeronautics
	G	Power Machinery
	G	Marine Navigation
	G	Moulding and casting of metals
15.00	G	Machine tools
	2	Endless screen papermaking machine
	2	Astronautics
	3	Computers
	open air	Rescue cruiser *(Summer only)*
15.30	G	Locomotives
	1	Plastics (Industrial Chemistry)
16.00	G	High-Voltage plant
	6	Zeiss-Planetarium *(Tickets at Information Desk)*
20.00 and 21.00		Observatory *(East dome, Entrance in museum courtyard) Saturday from Oktober to March (on clear nights)*

Programme subject to changes. Please read daily information display.

Guided tours and school parties are organized by the Tours Office, tel. 2179-252. Please apply in writing at least one week in advance. Special tours last about two hours and are limited to 25 people per group. The Volkshochschule (Adult Education Institute) leads a tour every Sunday from 11.00 to 13.00.
Free tours of the museum library take place each 2nd Sunday of the month at 11.00.

Photography (including flash) and use of *video cameras* are permitted for private purposes. Commercial photography, sound recordings and television recordings must be arranged with the Press Office, tel. 2179 250. A fee is payable in such cases.

Handicapped visitors. Most of the exhibition rooms are accessible to wheelchairs via ramps and lifts. Steps and stairs are indicated on the floor plans. Toilets for the handicapped are situated on the ground floor (near the entrance) and the first floor (near the Musical Instruments department). The lift to the restaurant is reached from the snack bar on the ground floor.

The *Forum der Technik* (Technology Forum) in the congress building consists of an IMAX cinema, a new planetarium, lecture and seminar rooms, and special exhibition rooms. Tel. 211250.

Special events (matinées, lectures, etc.) are announced in the quarterly programme of events which can be obtained from the Special Events Office, tel. 2179-246.

Food and drink
The *restaurant* between the ground floor and the first floor offers international cuisine, and is mainly self-service.
The *snack bar* on the ground floor is self-service. This is the only place in the museum where you may eat your own food.
The *cafeteria* on the 3rd floor is open until 16.00 for drinks and light refreshments. It has a view of the mountains in suitable weather conditions.
The *dining car* behind the museum is open in the summer for drinks and light refreshments.
For reservations telephone 416 8331.

When dialling any of the above Munich numbers from outside the city, but within Germany, use the code 089.

Open daily from 9.00 to 17.00. *Closed* on 1 January, Shrove Tuesday, Good Friday, Easter Sunday, 1 May, Whit Sunday, Corpus Christi, 1 November, 24, 25 & 31 December. On the 2nd Sunday in December from 9.00 to 14.00 only.

The ground floor is mainly dedicated to the classical fields of technology whose history stretches back thousands of years. These include mining, hydraulic engineering, the construction of roads, canals, bridges and tunnels, metallurgy, and marine navigation. The gradual process of industrialization can be witnessed, from simple lathes and windmills to motors and turbines and the use of electrical power and mineral oil. Parallel developments in the history of overland transportation are illustrated by examples of carriages, railway engines (both originals and models), automobiles and motorcycles.

The Ground Floor is not only huge, but a real labyrinth, and visitors will need a certain amount of time and stamina as they descend into the depths of the building in order to visit the Mining Department (which is on three separate levels) the Department of Marine Navigation (in the Basement and Ground Floor) and the Department of Automobiles and Motorcycles. In the Railways Hall and Power Machinery Hall, there are also balconies to be scaled. The traditional highlights remain the mines, the high-voltage demonstrations, and the world's first automobile: the Benz

Welding and Soldering ●

Materials Testing ●

● Machine Tools

Metallurgy

Mining ↓

Power Machinery ● Marine Navigation

Electrical Power ●

● Environment

Mineral Oil and Natural Gas

Hydraulic Engineering (1998) ●

● Entrance Hall

● Museum Shop

BASEMENT

three-wheeler. The narrow passageways in the Marine Navigation department contain a surprise around each corner; the Department of Mineral Oil and Natural Gas, with its own basement, and the Bridge Building exhibition (to be opened in 1988), should not be missed either. In the tower of the Deutsches Museum, there is an example of Foucault's pendulum, made famous in a novel of the same name by Umberto Eco.

To the left of the main entrance hall, the Environment department deals with vital contemporary issues. The museum's own green space behind the main building contains a windmill, a dining car serving light refreshments, the Theodor Heuss rescue cruiser and a historic radio telescope, and many other attractions. Although the aircraft in the Aeronautics Hall can be glimpsed from here, resist the temptation to visit them now, as they are described on page 81.

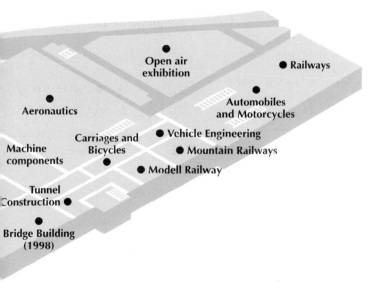

- Open air exhibition
- Railways
- Aeronautics
- Automobiles and Motorcycles
- Vehicle Engineering
- Carriages and Bicycles
- Machine components
- Mountain Railways
- Modell Railway
- Tunnel Construction
- Bridge Building (1998)

Our environment is subject to many different kinds of stress. The exhibition deals with possible solutions, provides a brief introduction to ecology, and documents the recent increase in environmental awareness.

The growth in global population from the dawn of history to the present day is illustrated by a model. Some of the exhibits address the issue of energy consumption. The industrialized nations, for example, make up only a quarter of the world's population, but use three quarters of the total energy produced.

The two models of a typical 19th century and 20th century kitchen demonstrate the change from mechanical to electrical equipment, the demand for greater convenience, and the resulting increase in energy requirements.

The first part of the exhibition is devoted to ecology and the laws of nature. The natural world is highly susceptible to harmful outside forces, comprising as it does a complex network of dynamic ecosystems, food chains, balanced exchange processes and internal buffers.

There are displays on the problem of air pollution and on some of the proposed solutions and remedies.

The effects of acid rain on the horribly disfigured late-gothic statue of Eve are all too apparent. Recent measures to reduce the concentrations of sulphur dioxide and nitrogen oxide have been aimed at preventing acid rain and the build-up of various types of smog in cities such as London and Los Angeles. The greenhouse effect, sustainable energy sources and domestic energy-saving measures are also dealt with. Various charts and graphic displays discuss the depletion of the ozone layer, examine the use of CFCs, and propose possible alternatives.

Other exhibits address the issues of erosion, waste, the threat to biodiversity by the dependence on monocultures, the widespread use of slash and burn techniques in forest clearance, and other stresses on the environment. The multimedia tower provides information on the subject of water. Next to a cube of compressed scrap metal – all that remains of a car – videos on automobile recycling and the treatment of effluents may be watched. *bh*

▷ Late gothic statue of Eve with plaster reconstruction
▷ One person's annual waste
▷ Population growth

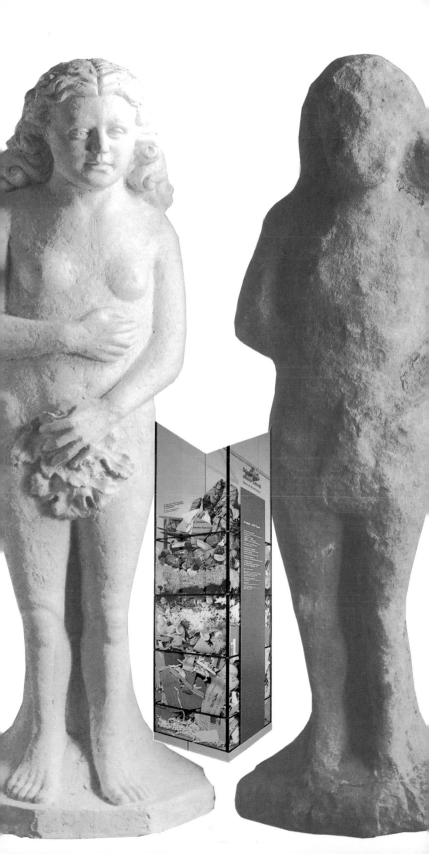

Mineral oil or 'petroleum' occurs naturally in the form of pitch, tar, or bitumen and has been used as a sealing and building material or for medicinal purposes for thousands of years.

The systematic search for oil began as the industrial revolution gathered pace. Germany's first successful borehole was sunk near Celle in the spring of 1859 by Prof. Georg C.K. Hunaeus. In August of that year, Edwin Drake struck oil in North America.

Mineral oil and natural gas are formed by the accumulation of the decomposing remains of large quantities of marine micro-organisms. The exhibition explains the conditions necessary for the creation of liquid and gaseous hydrocarbons and illustrates how they form enriched and economically exploitable reserves.

Geological prospecting and geophysical prospecting are used to reveal the geological structure of the earth's crust and exactly where oil or gas are likely to occur. Various displays explain the seismic, magnetic and gravimetric methods of exploration drilling and how they are used in oil prospecting.

When 'hopeful' subsurface structures are discovered, drilling is carried out to ascertain the levels of concentration of oil and gas. Drilling techniques are therefore closely related to the extraction of oil.

The first accounts of drilling originate from China. Using a cable or rope, depths of up to 500 m were achieved. The same method was still in use in the 19th century for opening up oil reservoirs in North America. Percussive drilling, in which a free-falling bit known as a 'jumper' is dropped into the borehole and shatters the rock at the bottom, was replaced by rotary drilling at the beginning of the 20th century. This method uses a rotating drill bit to grind away the rock. Several models illustrate the history of this drilling method. The exhibition is dominated by part of a rotary drilling unit, consisting of a swivel, mounted on a travelling block, and a rotary table. Together they weigh about 8 tons.

During the first few decades of oil production, the oil companies were satisfied with the quantities produced. Oil flowed readily from the well due to natural pressure in the reservoir. Today, pumps are used to increase the pressure

◁ Dahlbusch rescue 'bomb', 1963
▷ Rotary drilling unit, 1976

on the deposit by the injection of water, steam and chemical additives which help to release as much oil as possible from the reservoir rock. A so-called 'plunger pump' is on display. As the demand for oil and gas continues unabated, reserves under the sea bed have assumed increased importance. Special ships, and equipment such as drilling platforms, drilling vessels, production platforms, and pipe laying barges are shown in a large model of offshore oil production. The next section uses flow charts to explain the processes involved in the refining of petroleum and processing of crude oil. A large model of the refinery built at Wilhelmshaven in 1975 shows the com-

plex nature of a modern oil refinery.

In its natural form, crude oil is a mixture of many chemical compounds, most of which are hydrocarbons. Crude oil must first be treated, in order for consumable products to be obtained. The four main stages in the refining process are:

- Distillation, in which the constituents of crude oil are separated according to their various boiling points (gasolines, petroleum, etc.)
– Cracking the distillation residues, which produces additional fuel types and middle distillates
– Refining the crude oil derivatives
– Reforming, in order to improve fuel quality.

Follow the line painted on the floor to the gallery in order to see an original wooden barrel. A 'barrel', or 159 litres, is now an international measure in

△ Horse-drawn tank truck, 1909

◁ Filling pump, 1938

▷ Offshore drilling, 1976

the petroleum industry. Today, pipelines and supertankers are used to transport mineral oil and natural gas.

Petroleum products have to be stored before they reach the consumer. Surface storage, in tank farms, and subterranean storage of natural gas in underground caverns, are some of the main methods. There is a model of a tank farm, an explanation of underground storage techniques, and a description of the various ways crude oil and petroleum products are transported. The next section illustrates the uses of mineral oil, natural gas, and fuel products as used in the petrochemical industry. Various lamps and burners are evidence of domestic and industrial applications. The petrochemical industry uses oil and gas as raw materials for making plastics, solvents and lubricants. The exhibition focusses mainly on the production of acetylene, and olefines and aromatic substances. The section on the environ-

ment explains how pollutants, are produced and spread, and deals with the monitoring of pollution levels and environmental protection measures taken to protect precious natural resources such as air and water. The use of tank protectors and oil separators, the development of techniques aimed at producing optimum combustion, and the use of catalytic converters are discussed. There is also an explanation of some of the methods used to clean up oil spills. Deep drilling is the subject of a separate exhibition in a small room in the basement area. The set-up and operation of a drilling site varies according to the purpose of the site itself. Simple drilling machinery is used for foundation test boring, whereas specialized plant is required for prospection boring, exploration drilling and production wells. A special exhibition examines the role of relief wells and drilling methods used in rescue operations. *kf*

The Mining Department consists of a series of realistic and historically authentic scenes depicting working conditions in a mine. Original equipment and machinery from all periods of European mining can be seen. The visitor can experience at first hand a vital aspect of the history of civilization: the extraction and exploitation of mineral resources by mankind.

At the entrance to the mine, there is a Kind-Chaudron type shaft-sinking device, built in 1914. This 'trepan' made it possible to sink shafts through water-bearing strata for the first time.

The actual tour begins with a replica of a 19th century chapel, visited by miners before and after work, and continues with reproductions of wooden pit-props as used in mines in Germany and Poland. The visitor can also peer into shafts as they would have been sunk around 1925 – lined with masonry or cast iron rings known as 'tubbings' and drained by steam-driven pumps. In the early days of mining, winding (of materials) and haulage (of miners) were exhausting and time-consuming activities.

A reproduction of the reversible wheel as described by Georgius Agricola (1494–1554) in his twelve volume work on mining and foundries *De re metallica* indicates an early use of mechanization in mine shafts. Descending and ascending the shaft were made easier by Georg Dörell's invention of the 'man engine' which was used for hoisting miners. This part of the tour ends with a reconstruction of the pit bottom 750 m below the surface in the former Klenze mine shaft at the Hausham colliery, Upper Bavaria.

Primitive mining tools dating from prehistoric times and implements used more recently, as well as models of 19th century ore mines, trace the development of historic extraction and roadway driving methods. Various scenes depict 'driving' a tunnel by

◁ Chapel, 19th century
▷ Reversible wheel, 15th century
▷ Pit bank and man engine, 19th century

cast mining in the Stone Age and in the ancient world. The main example of open-cast mining techniques in loose rock is the open-cast lignite mine in Germany's Lower Rhine Basin. Open-cast techniques in solid rock are demonstrated by the iron ore open-cast mine in the Austrian province of Styria. Along with explanations of technical developments, there are examples of 'recultivation', i.e. the recreation of natural habitats on the sites of depleted open-cast mines.

hammer and chisel, winning ore by fire-setting, and how mines were drained by the goblin engine, a 16th century water raising machine. The transportation of ore by barge on underground drainage adits, and the extraction of ore by the longwall stoping method are illustrated, as are the principles of 'dialling' or mine surveying.

The section devoted to open-cast mining begins with a historical introduction to the earliest techniques of open-

Salt has played a vital part in the history of civilization. This mineral was originally mined purely for nutritional purposes; today, salt is an important raw material used by the chemical industry and in the production of artificial fertilizers.

The mine demonstrates how salt is won. There are reconstructions of a natural and an artificially contained salt spring, and a model of the well-house at the saline works in Bad Reichenhall. The

spraying pumps and sink-works explain how salt can be released from underground beds by means of water and pumped to the surface as brine with a salt content of 26%.

In the 18th century, pure rock salt was also mined by pillar and chamber work. The reconstruction shows the room-work at Wieliczka near Cracow in the 18th century. The extraction chamber of a potash mine (around 1925) leads to a small cinema, situated in a replica of a tunnel found in the Hattorf potash mine.

The section on coal mining begins with the extraction of 'pitch' or bituminous coal in Upper Bavaria around 1900. Mining techniques of the 1950s are illustrated by an engine room containing a winding engine used for blindshaft winding. A 'blind-shaft' is a winding shaft which connects individual galleries of the mine but does not reach the surface.

The rotary percussion drill and rocker shovel loader demonstrate the introduction

△ Manual shaft sinking, 1925
◁ Driving a tunnel with hammers and chisels, 19th century
◁ Ore transport by barge, 19th century
▷ Working an inclined seam, 20th century

The final part of the mine is devoted to modern coalmining and the extraction of ore by the room-work method. There is part of a roadway – a main traffic and transportation route driven either by blasting or machine, an overhead monorail used for conveying miners and materials, water tank explosion barriers, and a scene showing a mine's rescue services in action. In the roadway, there is a road-heading machine, as well as equipment used to transport coal and dead rock. At the coal face itself, armour-plated shield supports and a double drum shearer loader can be seen.

The subject of drill and blast work is dealt with at the tailgate, the end of the coal face. As the fallen rock accrues, it is loaded onto a drag conveyor by a side dump loader. In the room devoted to ore mining by pillar and chamber work, the three most important operations used underground are depicted: drilling the holes, stemming the holes, and conveying the ore after the controlled explosion.

The next room is devoted to extraction and hauling methods, and the development of rotary, churn, percussion and hammer drills, pick hammers, pit-props, mine carts and engines, and cutting machines and rams.

The products obtained by mining are raw materials. Ore-bearing rock has first to be separated from dead rock

of compressed air as the main form of drive for mining machinery. The next section gives a clear picture of working conditions for a miner in the 1950s. Facing work in steep seams is depicted, as are the difficulties involved in working a thin coal seam on a sublevel and a shallow seam with a compressed-air coal cutter and retarding disc conveyor. The introduction of mechanized extraction methods is illustrated by a coal plough and double chain conveyor.

△ Load haul dumper, 1977
◁ Drilling blast hole, 1925
▽ Drum shearer loader, 1900

and sized and graded before
any further metallurgical processing can take place. In the
section on ore dressing, original machinery, working models and dioramas illustrate
these processes. The final
room is dedicated to coal
treatment and deals with coal
as a raw material and source
of energy. The production
of brown coal briquettes,
coal gasification, fluid-bed
firing, and flue gas desul-
phurisation are all dealt with
here. *wk*

Mankind has been working with metals for about 10 000 years. The first known metals were those occurring in a pure, or 'natural' form, and which could be found lying on the ground. They attracted attention because they were unusually and processing of metals. Starting at the entrance to the mines, the development of metallurgy is traced from its very beginnings right through to the present day. The panorama in the first room highlights some of the main events in the history of metals

heavy, shiny, and could be easily worked. About 6000 years ago, man began to smelt metals from their natural compounds, the ores. Metals have properties which made them particularly attractive. Today, these materials are an indispensable part of life. In the introductory room, the visitor can find out about the properties of metals at first hand, and carry out simple experiments which demonstrate how metals conduct heat and electricity, their ductility, and ability to reflect light. The main part of the exhibition is concerned with the history of the manufacture up to the beginnings of the industrial age.

The manufacture of the 'oldest' metals such as copper and bronze and methods of working them such as forming (e.g. hammering) or casting are described. There follows an outline of the important metallurgical techniques used during the renaissance, as described by Georgius Agricola in his famous work on metallurgy *De re metallica*. These techniques remained largely unchanged until the industrial age. The most dramatic exhibits are the dioramas where the visitor can experience something of the atmosphere

of early smelting works and foundries. Historical displays of bloomery fires and shaft furnaces in the Siegerland lead to exhibits showing how pig iron was extracted in a blast furnace and steel was refined in a bloomery, or forge hearth. Forging, one of the most important forming techniques, is illustrated by the scythe forge. This was the eve of the industrial age.

The main exhibition hall deals with iron and steel, and is arranged chronologically. The first section takes us up to about 1850, when coal and coke replaced charcoal in the production of iron and steel. Steam power was also introduced around this time, and was used for blowers and forging.

The second section continues up to the mid-20th century and begins with a revolutionary breakthrough. For the first time, molten steel could be manufactured directly from pig iron. A Bessemer converter made this possible and a sectional view through one of these impressive pieces of equipment shows how liquid pig iron could be converted into steel. Another prime example of how steel is formed is the Mannesmann method of manufacturing seamless drawn tubes.

The third section deals with modern iron and steel

△ Historical part of the exhibition
◁ Bloomery fire in the Siegerland, 500 BC
▽ Water-jacket furnace, 1910

production. The first exhibit is a model of the newest type of blast furnace, Schwelgern II in Duisburg. Modern steel production is represented by a model of an oxygen blowing steel works and the continuous casting equipment, which dominates this part of the hall. Forming methods used today include forging, drawing, and rolling, all demonstrated by a series of machines. The nonferrous metals are dealt with individually, and there are subsections on the production

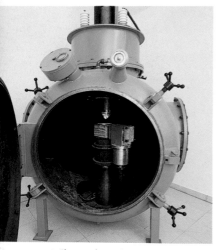

△ Electron-beam furnace, 1963
▷ Scythe mill, late 18th century
▷ Modern steel production, 1994

of copper, lead, zinc, alumini-
ım, and the refractory metals
ch as tungsten, tantalum,
niobium. Various smelting
ɔds used in metallurgy
ained, including the
haft furnace, open
ace, converter pro-
ectrolysis. Exhi-
mall water-

jacket furnace, parts of a zinc muffle furnace, and electrolytic cells. Traditional methods for refining ores, such as the use of an open hearth or 'reverberatory' furnace, are contrasted with modern ones such as roasting and smelting. The recycling of scrap metal is also dealt with here.

The area devoted to refractory metals explains why they cannot be manufactured in normal furnaces and describes the specialised smelting and refining methods necessary for their manufacture. Among the exhibits are part of an electron-beam furnace for refining special metals and a hydrogen reduction furnace. Important examples of modern forming methods are aluminium extrusion (demonstrated by a working model) and continuous casting and rolling of zinc sheet.

The methods used in powder metallurgy allow the manufacture of complicated components from metal powders. In the gallery overhead, there is a powder press and a model of a sintering oven.

Surface finishing, represented by part of a strip galvanising plant, reunites ferrous and non-ferrous metal production. Demonstrations of modern moulding and casting techniques mark the end of the exhibition.

Short films on the extraction of metals and various methods of forming steel and aluminium can be called up on five monitor screens. *kf*

Welding and soldering are techniques used to join metals. They are among the oldest production processes and date back at least 6000 years. Several hundred welding and soldering methods have been developed this century, of which about fifty are in common use. The most important methods are demonstrated, partly with the aid of working models. There is an important distinction between fusion welding and pressure welding. In the former, the weld is molten; in the latter, it is of a pasty consistency. In fusion welding, a gas flame or electric arc heats the area of the joint and fuses the additional or 'weld' metal. The joint is obtained by the flow of this molten substance, without pressure. In pressure welding, the joint is created by the application of extreme pressure to the parts to be joined, but usually without any weld metal being used. A series of welded workpieces demonstrates the

△ Arc welder, 1889
◁ Electric fusion welding, 1985

characteristics of the various types of welded joint known as 'seams'.

Soldering allows different materials, including non-metallic ones, to be joined by means of a molten binder, called 'solder', and flux. Today, this takes place on fully automatic production lines, illustrated by the enlarged photograph forming the backdrop of a large showcase containing various types of solder and flux. *ka*

Materials testing covers the following fields: the testing and improvement of new materials, detecting defects for the metal industry, investigation of damage to metal parts, and important research into the theory of the strength of materials.

The basic principles of materials testing have been understood for about 100 000 years, ever since man began to shape tools from stone. The scientific foundation only dates

back about 2300 years, when Archimedes formulated the laws of the properties of materials. Between the 16th and 18th centuries, scientists such as Galileo Galilei, Robert Hooke and Charles Coulomb conducted further investigations and added to the scientific knowledge of materials testing. Today, we distinguish between destructive and non-destructive testing, depending on the properties to be investigated or the methods used. Metals are vitally important

materials, and the department houses an impressive collection of testing equipment and samples. Many of the machines are of special historic interest, such as August Wöhler's tensile fatigue testing machine built in 1860, and some equipment still used by industry today, for example the UEDE 40 universal testing machine, which dates from 1974. *ka*

△ Samples of rail bending, 1925
△ Wöhler's tensile fatigue testing
   machine, 1860

The development of cutting machine tools from the 18th century to modern computer-controlled machine tools introduced in the mid-1980s is presented in three exhibition rooms. All the items of equipment are in working condition and can be demonstrated on request by museum staff, who will also explain how they function. The model of the bow drill is a reconstruction based on an Egyptian relief dating from the 4th millennium BC. It is the earliest known example of a drilling fixture. The development of drilling and turning equipment over the last 1000 years is illustrated by four dioramas. Lathes, planing and milling machines, and gear-cutting machines from the 18th and 19th centuries, are laid out as they would have been in a workshop of the time. Most of the machines are driven by gears from a common connecting shaft and are in good working order.

By 1930, most types of machine tool had already been developed. Any new advances and innovations, however, were to be made only after 1945. The machines produced after the war were distin-

guished by a more rigid, vibration-free construction, high dimensional stability, and greater driving power.

The second room is a faithful reproduction of a metalworking shop of

the 1950s and 1960s, even down to the detail of the fluorescent lighting typical of the day. The most modern machine tools are exhibited in the third room. Of particular interest are the groups of milling, turning, grinding, and eroding machines, the laser machining equipment which achieves the same precision as a five-axle milling machine, and a model of a computerized factory.

The model contains many moving parts and demonstrates the entire production process of a single part, from receipt of order, through the design and construction stages, right up to quality control and distribution. *ka*

◁ Bow drill, 4th millennium BC
◁ Machining centre, Lasercav, 1990
△ Metal turning lathe 1954
△ Workshop, 19th century

Engines are machines which convert various forms of energy into mechanical energy, normally in the form of rotary motion, so that it can be used to drive other machinery. The exhibition contains different types of engines, laid out in historical order. The visitor should begin with engines which use muscle power. In agriculture, skilled trades, mining, and transportation, some sort of mechanical power is needed. It was originally provided by the pure muscle power of humans and animals. Simple devices such as the lever, wedge, pulley, shaft, and wheel made possible a more efficient use of muscle power. Several such devices can be combined in engines using muscle power, as illustrated by the gin-driven mangle used in a dye house. Around this exhibit are arranged other typical examples of this type of engine, including cage wheels, treadwheels and other

gins. The first machines capable of transforming the power of running water into rotary motion were the undershot waterwheels, illustrated here by the model of a Franconian scoop wheel. The efficiency of waterwheels was increased by using artificial channels and better designs. Built into the wall are examples of overshot wheels, a breast wheel and a

waterwheel using wooden spoons. The next exhibits are the water column machines, in which pressurized water is used to drive the pistons. They represent a transition, technically and within the exhibition, to the piston steam engines. Grouped around a high-speed wind wheel built in 1905, a series of models documents the key stages in the development of wind power. This type of propulsion may be traced back as far

△ Ox treadwheel, about 1600
▷ General view of the exhibition
▷ Corn mill with spoon wheel, about 1870

as the 7th century AD, if we do not include the sail, which is much older.

About 250 years ago, the demand for mechanical energy could no longer be met by muscle, wind, and water alone. New sources of energy had to be found and new machines invented. One such machine, actually *the* machine of the 18th century, is the steam engine.

dating from the second half of the 19th century are displayed on the next level of the hall; opposite them are the steam turbines, which were introduced in the 1880s.

Steam boilers are displayed in the basement, where the related topics of their effect on the environment, and environmental protection measures are also discussed.

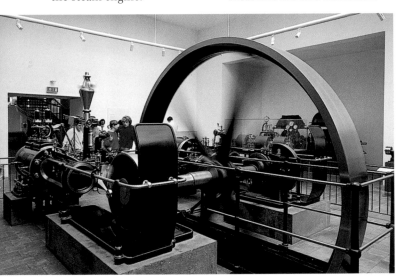

The double-acting industrial steam engine with rotary motion built by James Watt in 1788 was to have a decisive influence, not just in industry. An accurate reconstruction of this engine, together with the oldest surviving steam engine in Germany, which dates from 1813, and a valve-operated steam engine built by the Sulzer brothers in 1865, are the main attractions in this part of the room. The more advanced or 'perfected' steam engines

△ Twin compound steam engine, 1899
▷ First Diesel engine, 1897
▷ Jumo 004 B turbojet, 1944

Water turbines transform water power to driving energy with nearly no frictional loss. Alongside historic turbines, there are working models and originals of the Francis, Pelton, and Kaplan turbines, the main types in use today. These turbines can cope with water heads of up to 2000 m and

GROUND FLOOR

high flow rates of up to 900 m³ per second.

One result of the various attempts to find an economical source of power for smaller workshops was the hot-air engine. The first patent was granted in 1816 to Robert Stirling, who also gave his name to a whole class of engines. Hot-air engines were, however, unable to compete with innovations such as the internal combustion engine, which was developed in the 1860s. This still holds true today. Unfortunately, the impact on the environment of the different types of machine shown here was not really considered at the time.

The internal combustion engine functions as follows: a mixture of fuel and air is ignited in a closed combustion chamber; the explosive combustion produces burning gases and a subsequent build-up of pressure which drives the piston; the linear motion of the piston is then converted to rotary motion, usually by means of a crank. Within the exhibition, the engines are divided into Otto or 'spark-ignition' engines, Diesel or 'compression-ignition' engines, and rotary-piston engines. The first Diesel engines, as well as some very early engines by Otto, Daimler, Maybach, and Wankel, are among the most valuable objects in the collection. The tour ends with the gas turbines and jet engines. In both these types of engine, the

mechanical energy required is produced by an accelerated stream of gas resulting from heating compressed air in combustion chambers. In the gas turbine it gives up its energy to a rotor mounted on a shaft which can drive, for example, a generator, pump, or the blades of a helicopter. In the jet engine, the gas emerges through a nozzle at high velocity and drives an aircraft or rocket by the recoil effect of the combustion gases. For reasons of space, only a few typical examples of this type of engine can be shown. *er*

The term machine components is used today to cover parts meeting standard specifications as used in the construction of technical apparatus. Individual components, such as screws, as well as entire assembly groups such as gear transmissions are included. The exhibition focusses on two main areas: drives, and kinematics –

examples in the exhibition. Among the most conspicuous exhibits is a reconstruction of the first machine for producing ball bearings (1893). The motions of 62 sliding and rolling bearings can be easily observed. There is also a collection of electrically driven models of chain and belt drives. The central exhibit is a working series of universal and constant-velocity joints. In addition, there are many different kinds of clutches and gears, shown both in cross-section and as working models. A four-wheel-drive tractor has been partially cut away in order to illustrate how several thousand machine components can be used in combination. Finally, a comprehensive collection of locks and keys cover 2000 years of the locksmith's art. *ka*

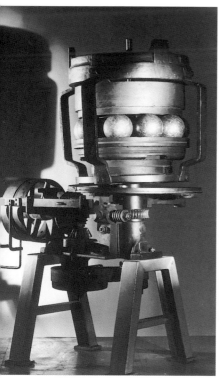

(ncluding the theory of motion and especially mechanisms. Historic models made by Franz Reuleaux, the father of modern kinematics, are of great significance. The complicated motions of the various types of drive can best be understood by studying the

△ Lock and key from a church, 18th century
◁ First ball-bearing grinding machine, 1893
▽ Frictional drives, about 1900

This exhibition extends over two rooms and outlines the main stages in the generation and distribution of electrical energy, and its beneficial effects to the consumer. The underlying physical process is the conversion of mechanical energy to electrical energy, based on the principle of electromagnetic induction, a phenomenon discovered by Michael Faraday in 1831. The discovery of the dynamo-electric principle, made independently by Werner Siemens, Alfred Varley, and Charles Wheatston in 1866 brought further progress.

Over the years, consumers had become familiar with accumulator batteries and had begun to trust direct current (DC). To begin with, only DC systems were set up with generating stations supplying the immediate neighbourhood. However, the increasing use of electric motors created a greater requirement for energy than electric lighting had demanded. A need arose for larger generators, and methods were soon devised to transform both voltage and current and supply electricity from conveniently situated, remote power stations to the rapidly growing conurbations. Since the invention of the alternating current (AC) transformer in 1885 by three Hungarian engineers, Otto Blathy, Max Deri and Carl Zipernowsky, the power output of generators has grown from a few kilowatts (KW) to over a thousand megawatts, and transmission voltages from a few hundred volts to several hundred thousand volts. New equipment had to

▽ The path of the current, 1953

be designed and built to match.

In accordance with these developments, three main engineering disciplines emerged: electrical machines, electrical systems, and high-voltage technology. In the first room, the historical beginnings and subsequent development of electrical machinery are illustrated. Beginning with the original Siemens dynamo, improvements were made which led to increasingly efficient machinery. There are also demonstrations of the typical operating conditions of DC and AC machines: starting, speed regulation, and braking.

Oskar von Miller, the founder of the Deutsches Museum, also made important contributions to electrical engineering, and these are examined in this room and the next. He carried out the first two major trials of long-distance power transmission: The 1400 V direct current transmission from Miesbach to Munich over a distance of 57 km in 1882, and the 15 000 V three-phase

▷ Three-phase generation and
   distribution
▷ High-voltage plant and simulated
   stroke of lightning
▽ The first dynamo, W. Siemens, 1866

transmission from Lauffen to Frankfurt in 1891. He also supervised the construction of the first hydro-electric scheme in the Alps, the Walchensee power station, built in 1924.

The second room outlines the history of electrical systems engineering; the most important stages in its development are represented by a number of exhibits, including: generators and their protective devices, switching equipment, transformers, cables, overhead lines, and the claw-pole type generator used for the three-phase transmission from Lauffen to Frankfurt. Twelve large display boards explain the economic importance of electrical power engineering, a field known as electro-economics, and how a coherent network in the form of an international grid system has been created. Stretching from the North Cape to Sicily, it is designed to distribute 220 000 megawatts in parallel operation.

The demonstrations of high-voltage apparatus take place three times a day and are one of the most popular attractions in the museum. The public can familiarize itself with electrical power engineering and understand how 50 Herz AC voltages of 300 000 V are produced and impulse voltages of up to 800 000 V lasting a mere two microseconds are created and used to simulate a stroke of lightning. *fb*

The exhibition on hydraulic engineering and water management is currently being rearranged, and is expected to open in May 1998. Water is essential to all forms of life on earth, and the department seeks to demonstrate how mankind has exploited this resource, using a number of examples taken from civil engineering projects. Our relationship to water is clearly shown, on the one hand, by the

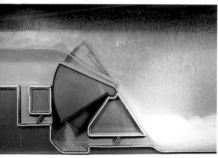

ways in which we attempt to secure a steady supply of water for drinking purposes and general use, the use of waterways for the transfer of goods, and the use of water as a source of energy, and, on the other hand, by the protection of human habitats from the constant threat of flooding. The protection of this precious resource from the effects of human activities has become an equally important topic. The exhibition concentrates on the dilemma posed by water's threatening, primeval and to some extent still untamed forces, and how this power may be harnessed

in a responsible way. Thus, the themes of exploitation and protection, recreation and enjoyment are all covered. Ecological topics are also addressed in connection with the engineering projects discussed.

Diagrams and experiments explain water's natural cycle and man's intervention in this self-perpetuating system. A major theme of the exhibition is canals and river engineering; it covers all types of intervention in the natural world by engineering aimed at improving our habitat.

Successful irrigation and the use of water as a sustainable source of energy are presented in terms of the decisive role they play in the technological and social development of human communities. River correction, hydraulic engineering projects, sluices, weirs, locks, and dam construction are all illustrated by means of dioramas, models, and experiments.

Qualitative water management is the other main subject dealt with in the exhibition. Best understood as a regulated water cycle functioning within the natural one, the management of water has assumed an increasingly significant role. *db*

△ Sector weir, 1962
▷ Dam construction works (upper level), at Kaprun, 1962
▷ Weir defense, about 1930

For thousands of years, travel and the transport of goods not involving waterways were arduous undertakings. The invention of the wheel in prehistoric times only became significant when the use of horse-drawn vehicles and carriages was made possible by an expanding network of roads constructed during the Roman Empire. These roads fell into such disrepair in the Dark Ages that travelling on horseback became the preferred mode of transport. Before 1500, vehicles were not fitted with spring suspension. The construction of the carriage soon banished this discomfort, however.

The wish to travel further and faster than our feet will allow was fulfilled by the invention of the bicycle over one hundred years ago. It makes possible a fourfold increase in the distance we can travel and, not surprisingly, is the most common vehicle in the world. Bicycles built at the turn of the century resemble very much those of today. In its present form, which was introduced about 1886, the bicycle replaced the 'ordinary', or 'penny farthing', a fast but highly dangerous piece of equipment. As the diameter of the front wheel increased and breakneck speeds were reached, the riders would often part company with their steed, leading to horrific accidents. The two-wheel bicycle only gained popularity with the 'low wheel'. Special designs appeared such as the 'ladies' bicycle', the 'racing bicycle', the 'tandem' and the 'folding cycle' for army use. The once-common pedal cars and tricycles only survived as children's toys. Bicycle design stimulated the entire vehicle construction industry. Lightweight tubular steel frames, the use of ball bearings in wheel hubs, pneumatic tyres and wire spokes were all tested for the first time on bicycles. The true forerunner of the automobile was not the coach, but the bicycle. *hs*

△ Drais 'hobby horse', 1817

▽ Carriage, about 1810

As the 20th century pro-gressed, the motorcar gradually became the world's most important means of transport. The Deutsches Museum's collection of 55 automobiles in the basement of the Railways Hall illus-trates the fascinating history of this means of trans-port. The most im-portant exhibit is the first motor vehicle capable

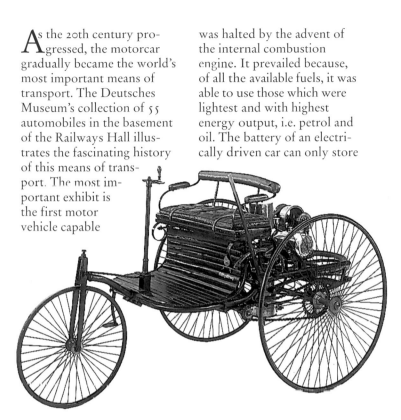

was halted by the advent of the internal combustion engine. It prevailed because, of all the available fuels, it was able to use those which were lightest and with highest energy output, i.e. petrol and oil. The battery of an electri-cally driven car can only store

of further development, Carl Benz' three-wheeler. This masterpiece was presented to the museum by the inventor himself, twenty years after his historic first journey through Mannheim in 1886. At least 30 replicas of this subtle piece of engineering have been built, but the original is here in the museum. Although it was no faster than a bicycle and less powerful than a horse, its source of power belonged to the future. Steam carriages may have been quieter, and electric cars cleaner, but their progress

△ Benz motor car, 1886

one hundredth as much energy as a fuel tank of the same weight. Our 1908 Baker Elec-tric had a range of only 50 km, for example, but had one advantage over the two coke-fired and oil-fired steam carriages: the owner could simply climb in and drive off, without needing at least a quarter of an hour to raise steam. The 'motorcars' were ridiculed as first, but soon proved their superiority in the first major trial held in France in 1895. The petrol, or gasoline engine was lighter and more powerful than other forms of propulsion. It drove the rear wheels and was therefore mounted between them. Six cars, built by Daimler, Benz, and Opel, all used this principle. The steering wheel had yet to be invented, and luxuries such as pneumatic tyres, doors and windscreens belonged to the future. The first true car, incorporating all these features, is a Mercedes. The era of the horseless carriage with its rear-mounted engine was over and the new automobiles – their engines mounted at the front – coasted smoothly into the 20th century. Wilhelm Maybach, the designer of the Mercedes, had created the model for the motorcar of the future. He placed a large radiator in front of the water-cooled engine, increasing its output to 45 horsepower. He was famous as a successful racing driver, which, in those days, was a measure of the reliability of a designer's cars. Whether it was a Berlin manufacturer such as Protos deciding to enter the 1908 round the world race, or Audi's *Alpensieger* (Alpine Champion) mastering the steepest Alpine passes in 1914, the publicity value was paramount. After the First World War, Mercedes once again gained an international reputation with its superchargers. The SS Type managed 175 kph on the racetrack, while on the road it resembled a luxury limousine. In 1930, it cost as much as a smart suburban house; today it would command about the same amount. Its creator, Ferdinand Porsche, subsequently devoted himself to racing cars and then to the concept of the Volkswagen, literally the 'people's car'. For Saxony's Auto-Union he designed the 520 hp Grand

▷ Audi *Alpensieger*, 1914
▷ Rumpler *Tropfenwagen*, 1921
▷ Lancia *Lambda*, 1923
▷ Opel 1.2 litre limousine, 1935
▽ Adler with wood-burning gas generator, 1938

Prix racing car with its 16-cylinder compressor engine mounted in front of the rear axle, and later, a robust 24 hp vehicle with

rear-mounted engine for the future Volkswagen company. The 'beetle' shape survived World War II and became the trademark of the car with the highest production figures in the history of the automobile industry. Even the Ford Model T, of which 15 million were built in Detroit between 1908 and 1927, was not produced in the same numbers, the 'Beetle'

outstripping it by 6 million. Henry Ford, however, takes the credit for introducing assembly-line production, which enabled him to reduce the vehicle price to that of a European motorcycle. He visited the Deutsches Museum in 1930 and promised to donate a Model T. At the time, America was manufacturing the largest number and the best cars in the world. Germany was at last able to acquire this expertise when Opel was taken over by the American company General Motors. The Opel P4 became even more popular than its predecessor which had earned the nickname 'Laubfrosch' – a greenback or treefrog, while the Olympia became one of the most advanced cars of its day. The 'integral' or self-supporting bodywork rendered a chassis unnecessary and replaced the wooden body with an all-steel construction. The saving in weight and improved safety were considerable. The department's Opel *Olympia* appears exactly as it was exhibited at the 1937 Berlin Motor Show, with

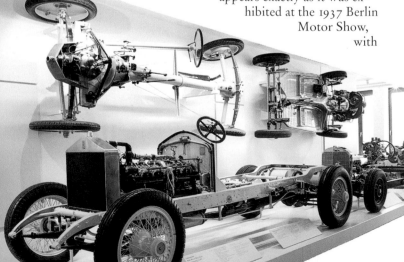

sections cut away and covered in glass. Berlin also produced the DKW F7 with its half-timbered bodywork. It was unusual in having front-wheel drive, the advantages of which were hotly debated for a good 50 years. Today the argument no longer rages – the energy savings are undeniable. Streamlining experienced troubled beginnings too. It only really came into its own after oil prices had risen steeply in the 1980s. From the 1921 *Tropfenwagen*, based on a 'teardrop' shape and built by the aircraft designer Edmund Rumpler, up to the final car to be built by NSU, the Ro 80, streamlining was much admired but did not sell well. Aerodynamic principles were accepted without any reservations only in aircraft design and racing car construction. The Mercedes *Silberpfeile*, or 'Silver Arrows' would hardly have reached 300 kph without their streamlined aluminium bodywork.

No industrial product has demanded such high development costs as the car. This has less to do with the technology involved, than with its advance from a luxury item to a common consumer product requiring enormous investments for its mass production. The development of subassemblies such as engine, chassis, and bodywork is illustrated by a

number of cut-away and working models. At the touch of a button, the chassis and bodywork of a BMW 325 are assembled and a robot fits the fourth door – the day to day production processes in a smoothly running factory. From its humble beginnings as a motorized bicycle, the motorcycle eventually reached

such a level of perfection that it became the 'poor man's car', at least until the advent of the expensive sports models in the 1960s. The engine dominates the appearance of all motorcycles, and the collection's 35 exhibits illustrate well the various engine designs, methods of mounting, and number of cylinders which have been tried. The summit of perfection was probably achieved with the BMW and NSU models which set respective world records of nearly 280 kph in 1937 and 340 kph in 1956. *hs*

△ Daimler Maybach motorcycle
◁ Porsche's 1938 Volkswagen
◁ Automobile chassis, 1922–1946

The Railways Hall contains many exhibits illustrating the design and development of rolling stock, such as steam, diesel and electric locomotives, as well as displays dealing with the logistics of the rail network, signalling and route safety, and rail and track engineering. A replica of one of the first operational steam locomotives, the *Puffing Billy*, is situated at the entrance to the hall. Built in 1814, it was used on an English colliery railway for almost fifty years. The next exhibit, the *Landwührden*, once belonged to the »Herzoglich Oldenburgische Staatsbahn« (Duchy of Oldenburg State Railway) and is technologically far superior, although the two engines obviously have much in common. While the *Landwührden*, manufactured in 1867, was the first locomotive to emerge from the workshops of the recently founded Krauss company, the express locomotive class BIX next to it dates from 1874 and was already the 1000th to be built by the Munich locomotive builders Maffei. The boiler and engine have been cut away and a brief glimpse is enough to understand the principles involved. This series of steam locomotives culminates in the Bavarian S 3/6, built in 1912 and probably the best-known passenger locomotive of the »Deutsche Länderbahnen« (German State Railways). It hauled famous trains such as the *Rheingoldexpress*, and was in operation until 1957.
The very early days of electric traction are represented by one of the most valuable items on display, the world's first electric locomotive, built by Werner Siemens for use in mines and first demonstrated on the narrow-gauge track of

▷ First electric locomotive, 1879
▷ LAG 1 local railway locomotive, 1905
▷ Bosnian rack locomotive, 1908
▽ *Puffing Billy*, 1814

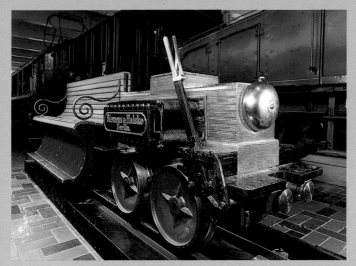

a park railway at the 1879 Berlin Trade Fair. On the main track next to it stands the first electric locomotive built to use high-voltage, single-phase alternating current, a system still in use in German-speaking countries and Scandinavia. The LAG 1 was manufactured in 1905 for Munich's »Lokalbahn Aktiengesellschaft« and used on a private branch line between Murnau and Oberammergau in Upper Bavaria. The next exhibits are the De 2/2, the first standard gauge locomotive using three-phase current, built for the Swiss Burgdorf-Thun railway in 1899, and an electric express locomotive, the E16, built in 1927 for the »Deutsche Reichsbahn« (German Imperial Railways). It has an interesting driving mechanism: the transmission of power takes place by the so-called Buchli drive, which balances the spring between driving axle and motor. At the end of the track there is a locomotive which uses a new type of drive, the V 140 Diesel with hydrodynamic power transmission linking the massive 16-cylinder diesel engine and the driving axles. Built in 1935, and with an engine producing over 1000 KW, she was not only a match for the steam engines of her day, but superior in operational terms too. This locomotive represents the beginnings of a technical revolution which was continued for many decades by the »Deutsche Bundesbahn« (German Federal Railways). Underneath the nearby gallery is the drive unit of a modern diesel locomotive class 216. The engine, gears, and cardan shafts are also displayed. An entirely different principle was used by MBB in 1971 for

▽ Historic locomotives

trials of its prototype train, the *Prinzipfahrzeug,* or 'Principle Vehicle' which operated by magnetic levitation. The first experiments in this field date back to the 1930s. Magnetic levitation trains advance without mechanical contact of the vehicle with the guideway and are, in principle, technically superior to the conventional wheel-on-rail system. Their advantage remains relative, however, as air resistance is still a limiting factor at very high speeds.

At the far end of the hall, there is a survey of signalling and track safety, beginning with early mechanical signals and signal boxes and including electromechanical track safety systems as well as modern light signals and panel-operated signal boxes. There is a display on track engineering underneath the left-hand gallery, next to the exit leading to the outdoor exhibits area. Part of a track with longitudinal sleepers and iron bedding plates depicts the type of track laying methods used at the beginning of the European railway era. It previously belonged to the Austro-Hungarian »k.k. privilegierte Erste Eisenbahngesellschaft« (First Railway Company by Royal and Imperial Appointment) which opened the first section of the Linz-Budejovice line in 1828. A series of sleepers and tracks making up the permanent way, along with equipment and machinery for repair and renewal of the rails, demonstrate the wide-ranging developments in track engineering right up to the recent high-speed tracks using welded rails and concrete sleepers.

Along both galleries of the Railways hall, a brief synopsis of railway history documents the very early days through to the express traffic of the late twentieth century.

The most modern computer-controlled model railway in Europe has impressed visitors of all ages. Travelling over a total track length of nearly 300 m, more than 30 trains arrive at and depart from a number of different stations. Signals, track safety devices, the trains themselves and even the timetable are true to life, right down to the last detail. There is a serious side to this highly entertaining model:

nowhere else can the overall logistics of the railway network be so clearly demonstrated. The progress of each train can be followed on monitor screens and is registered by a central computer at over 260 separate photo-electric barriers, exactly as it would be in a modern signalling centre. The trains are guided through the complicated network precisely according to the timetable. Several TV cameras monitor shunting operations in the depot and train movements on discrete stretches of track. *ls*

▽ Viznau-Rigi rack-railway, 1871

Tunnels enable thorough-
fares to be constructed in
an unobtrusive way when
mountains or reaches of water
impede further progress. They
can also make city centres
more accessible, supply drinking water and carry off waste
water. In mining, they are used
in the extraction of raw materials. The triumphant advance
of the railways in the 19th century was mainly responsible
for rapid developments in
tunnel construction. In order
to protect the excavated spaces
from the weight of the rock or
earth above, they must be
secured during construction
with temporary supports and
by masonry when in perma-
nent use. Flooding must also
be prevented. Over the years,
a number of methods have
been developed, and these are
illustrated by means of replicas,
models, and demonstrations.
The tools used in tunnel construction, often of incredible
size, are a further topic of the
exhibition. Of increasing
importance nowadays is the
shield driving method, which
was developed

in the early 19th century. This
technique was employed in the
construction of the Munich
underground and the Channel
Tunnel, which called for the
use of enormous machines,
some of them fully automatic
and computer-controlled. *db*

△ Simplon tunnel, 1898–1905
▽ Fully mechanized shield driving used
during construction of the Munich
underground system

The exhibition on bridge building, which is scheduled to reopen in May 1998, examines the relationship between scientific findings, especially in the field of mechanics, and their practical application in construction engineering. Bridges exemplify supporting structures in their purest form. In the centre of the room, a bridge designed to vibrate as visitors walk across it forms a focal point of the exhibition. The motion of this observation bridge and the changes of shape it undergoes are reproduced on a multimedia display. It is based on a design by Prof. J. Schlaich. Using the interactive display as a point of departure, the three main areas of the exhibition can be explored. Each is devoted to a different method of construction used to support the bridge. These areas, arranged as three islands, illustrate the systems used for the construction of beam bridges, arched bridges, and suspension bridges. Pillars provide explanatory texts on construction methods and a synopsis of the history of bridge building. The development of bridge building methods is illustrated by models of important bridges chosen for their significant contribution to bridge construction.

A bridge's superstructure is characterised by the way the bridge is supported. Experiments illustrate the behaviour of structures under load and explain how the various components of a bridge function.

In the centre of each island, a model of a bridge under construction illustrates how a typical bridge is erected. An impressive example is a model showing the phases of the construction work for the stone bridge built over the Seine at Neuilly between 1768 and 1774 by Jean Rodolphe Perronet. One of the pioneers of modern bridge-building, he used a bold design which incorporates five arches. The two-storey multimedia display not only reproduces the flexing of the 'soft' bridge in the centre of the room, but also depicts scenes of the working environment of bridge builders. Work on a suspension bridge, from initial design to maintenance of the completed structure, may be seen in the lower section of the display. Finally, the subject of moving bridges is dealt with. Information appears

in the upper part of the display, and the visitor's best vantage point is from the observation bridge. Next to the displays on the load-bearing behaviour of the observation bridge are models of moving bridges. *db*

△ Bridge at Neuilly, 1768–1774
◁ Design by Prof. J. Schlaich for a
  soft bridge, 1995
▽ Elisabeth Bridge, Budapest, 1903

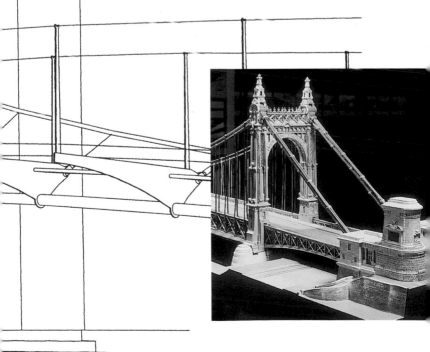

Throughout the history of mankind, ships have provided trading links between continents and thus between the cultures of their inhabitants. Well into the 20th century, ships were the only means of importing goods and obtaining information from overseas. A ship at sea is an isolated environment, a world

The development of sailing ships is traced along the left-hand side of the exhibition: from cogs which formed the trading fleet of the Hanseatic League, and caravels and three-masted sailing ships which reached all four corners of the globe and opened the way for the exploitation of natural resources, right up to tall ships

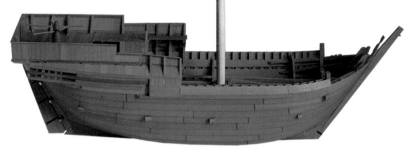

on its own. This is clearly illustrated by the living and working quarters of the fishing vessel *Maria* which dominates the exhibition. Known as an 'Ewer', she was built in 1880 for use in the North Sea and marks the end of an era, that of commercial sailing ships. From then on, steel hulls were adopted and mechanical propulsion – the trademark of the industrial age – prevailed. These developments are demonstrated by the steam tug *Renzo* (1932) at the end of the hall. The third ship of the exhibition, a rescue cruiser of the »Theodor Heuss« class (1960), is located just behind the museum. Thus, the three most important periods of shipping are represented: sail, steam, and diesel engine.

such as the *Preussen* (1902). The prestige of the industrial nations was represented by the powerful and luxurious passenger liners which were built at the turn of the century – the *Kaiser Wilhelm II* (1903) for example – or the *Europa* (1928), which won the coveted »Blue Riband« award. After aircraft took over the long-distance routes, the increase in road traffic created the need for car ferries such as the *Silja Europa* (1993). Models in the gallery overhead illustrate how bulk freighters are adapted to their particular cargo, whether general cargo, refrigerated produce, or bulk freight such

△ Hanseatic cog, about 1380
▷ The *Maria*, an Ewer built in 1880

as oil, coal or grain. After 1960, transshipment technology and container systems linked ocean shipping and inland navigation to road and rail, creating an integrated transport network.

Long before the industrial

age, rafts and barges on inland waterways were an important if not only the means of transport. Boats, which developed to meet local requirements, are mainly exhibited on the right-hand side of the ground floor. Boat builders used naturally available materials such as logs, reeds and animal hides, and the tools and styles of their region in characteristic ways to produce dug-outs, rafts, coracles, outriggers or elegant gondolas. Today's leisure-oriented society has revived these types of boat, and increasing numbers of people have taken up rowing and sailing, pitting themselves

once more against the wind and the waves. By standing on the front staircase leading to the basement, it is possible to look inside the *Maria* and see the crew's quarters and the 'fish bin', where the catch was kept alive and fresh in sea water. The next section offers a glimpse of life as a steerage passenger on board one of the ships which took millions of emigrants to the New World in the hope of a better life. There are also examples of sailors' hobbies, such as ships carved from bones and ships-in-a-bottle.

The subject of propulsion covers marine engines as well as propulsion devices such as paddlewheels and propellers. The steam engine from the Elbe steamer *Bohemia* (1853) is on display, so too is one of the first motorboats built by Gottfried Daimler (1886) and various outboard motors. Shipbuilding theory investigates the buoyancy, stability, and water resistance of a vessel. These properties are explained

△ Engine room of the steam tug *Renzo,* 1932
▷ Daimler motorboat, 1886
▽ *Silja Europa* cruiser and car ferry 1993

in demonstrations and in a model tank. Until the 19th century, shipbuilding was governed by traditional techniques used by the craftsmen who had built wooden ships. Along with the typical woodworking tools and types of construction, there is a series of models illustrating how ship design developed. A diorama shows the skills required by a ship's carpenter, from laying the keel to a ship's launch. Compare this to the next diorama showing a shipyard where steel ships were built a century later. Navigation is the art of setting a safe and economical course for a ship and maintaining it. In the early days of seafaring, ships stayed within sight of the coast and navigated by familiar landmarks. This proximity to the shore, however, brought its dangers – the history of shipping is also the history of shipwrecks. Various models deal with the subject of rescue at sea, carried out by vessels such as the rescue cruiser outside. One of the earliest navigation

instruments was the plumbline, used to measure the depth of water. The log was used to determine the speed of the ship relative to the water. As ships began to make journeys around the world, it became necessary to fix a ship's position and make geodetic measurements of ever increasing accuracy. Although the average speed of a journey by ship was no greater than walking pace, the rotation of the earth, which reaches a considerable 900 knots at the equator, caused enormous navigational problems when using instruments such as a sextant to measure angles and fix the latitude of the ship's position according to the course of the stars. The need to determine the exact longitude, which is based on local time, led to the development of the precision chronometer

in the 18th century.
The magnetic compass establishes cardinal points and has been in use since the 14th century. Variations in the earth's magnetic field, and disturbances caused by metal hulls led to the invention of the gyro-compass. The first one to be put into practical use, made by Hermann Anschütz-

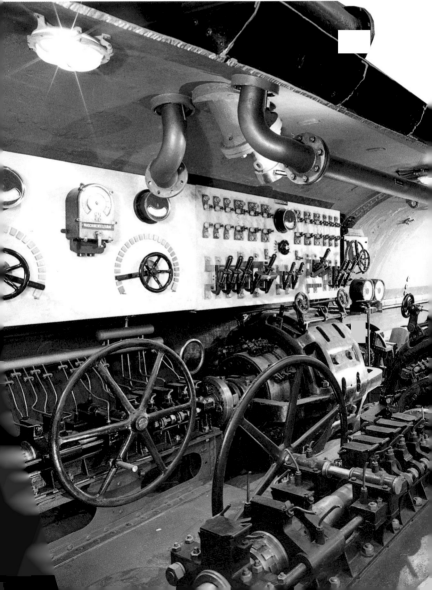

Kaempfe in 1908, is included in an extensive series of gyro-compasses. The forerunners of modern navigational methods are the echo-sounder and the radio beacons used as artificial landmarks.

The last part of the exhibition contains the 'men-of-war' and a replica battery deck. In the 19th and 20th centuries, many of the developments in military technology were the result of private initiatives. Wilhelm Bauer and his working model of a 'submersible boat' (1852) and Christian Hülsmeyer's first radar experiments with the Telemobilscope (1904) are good examples of this trend. The first German submarine, the U1 (1906), has been in the museum since 1921. Among the final exhibits is the Piccard brothers' bathysphere, which reached a record depth of 10 916 m in 1960. *jb*

△ Rescue cruiser, 1960
◁ Gyro-compass, 1908
◁ U1 submarine, 1906
▽ Piccard bathysphere, 1959

The first floor is dominated by the department of Aeronautics and vies with the ground floor in terms of popularity. The most famous aircraft in the world are exhibited here, including Lilienthal's original glider, and the legendary Junkers Ju 52. A jet engine built in the former German Democratic Republic is yet another important exhibit. Beginning with the balloons and hanging gliders on the first floor, the exhibition continues on the ground floor with jet aircraft and jet engines, helicopters, and the SPACELAB. The A4 rocket forms a natural link with the Department of Astronautics, and from here the propeller aircraft can best be viewed. Grouped around the aircraft halls are various other departments. From the Deutsches Museum Hall of Fame, the exhibition of Scientific Instruments may be reached. Devoted to Brander and Fraunhofer, it includes the telescope used to discover Neptune. In the Department of Physics, numerous experiments help explain the principles of mechanics, heat, electricity, optics, and atomic

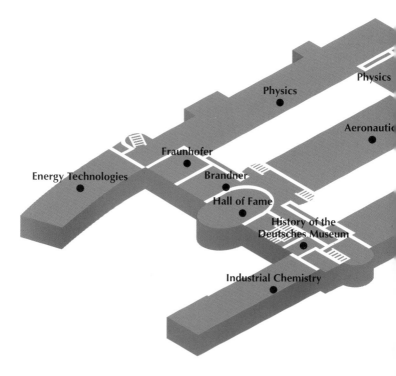

FIRST FLOOR

physics. The main attractions include apparatus used by Heinrich Hertz and Conrad Röntgen. On the other side of the Hall of Fame are the two departments of chemistry. In Scientific Chemistry, there are also plenty of experiments, a lecture theatre, a model of DNA, and the laboratory bench where, in 1938, Otto Hahn and his team of scientists discovered the principle of splitting the atom. Amid so much history, the story of the museum itself is not forgotten; it is told in the History of the Deutsches Museum, next to the entrance to Industrial Chemistry. Continuing through the Department of Scientific Chemistry and a small room for special exhibitions, the visitor enters the world of Musical Instruments and Automata. This exhibition, perhaps more than any other in the Deutsches Museum, illustrates the clear links between technology and civilization. The Siemens studio for electronic music and Baron Wolfgang von Kempelen's 'talking machine' from the 18th century are genuine rarities.

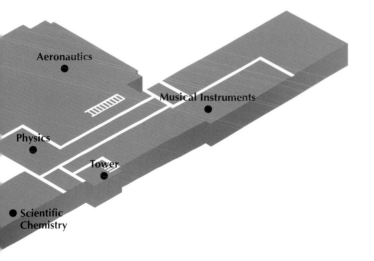

△ View of the exhibition

▽ Hall of Fame with busts, reliefs, and portraits

The art of scientific instrument-making flourished as never before in the 18th century, the age of enlightenment. For the first time, the market for such pieces of equipment was large enough to allow some manufacturers, particularly in London, Paris and the Netherlands, to develop and manufacture them commercially. In Germany, Georg Friedrich Brander (1713–1783) founded the most important workshop of the day. He supplied the Bavarian Academy of Sciences, numerous universities, and major Benedictine abbeys in southern German-speaking regions. The workshops became more specialized at the beginning of the 19th century. In Munich, Joseph Fraunhofer and Georg Reichenbach mainly built surveying instruments, but also instruments for astronomical observation which were the most accurate of the time. The concomitant rise of astronomy was due in part to the pendulum grinding machine designed by Reichenbach, which made it possible to build instruments to a much higher precision. Fraunhofer's discovery of the dark absorption lines in the solar spectrum led him to

develop a method which used various types of glass to measure the diffraction of white light into its constituent wavelengths by interference. The resulting achromatic lens telescopes led to numerous astronomical discoveries in the 19th century. *ab*

△ Azimuth quadrant by Brander, 1760
▽ Fraunhofer spectrum, 1814

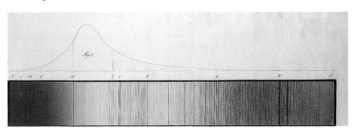

Mankind uses enormous quantities of heat, light, and motive power and also requires considerable amounts of power for telecommunications. This demand initiates a large number of energy conversion processes. The energy necessary for these processes to continue is mainly provided by burning fossil fuels.

is a primary concern and the disposal of radioactive waste a major problem. About one third of our electricity is currently generated by nuclear fission – the splitting of the nucleus of heavy atoms. The other method of producing energy by nuclear reaction is the so-called nuclear fusion of lighter atoms such as

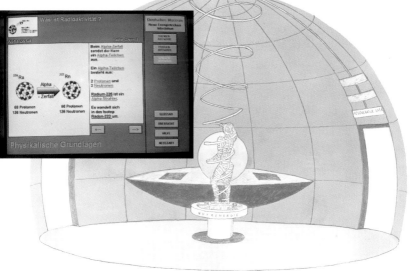

The carbon dioxide this releases has a long-term effect on our climate, however. In order to reduce emissions of CO_2 we have to use more efficient energy conversion systems or turn to renewable sources of primary energy which do not produce CO_2. What can we as individuals do to help? A computer game demonstrates how our energy consumption is influenced by our patterns of behaviour. The use of nuclear energy is a controversial subject. Although it does not release CO_2, safety

hydrogen. The necessary physical conditions for nuclear fusion to take place are, however, much more complicated than for nuclear fission. Fusion reactors are still in their experimental phase. Solar energy is a practically inexhaustible and global source of energy. Nature's plentiful reserves, however, are difficult to exploit due to local geographic variations and fluctuations in supply.

△ Entrance area
△ Atomic structure (interactive display)

What is your personal energy consumption?

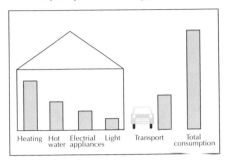

◁ The diagram shows the average energy consumption for a family of three.

The current level of solar radiation on the roof of the museum is displayed in the exhibition.

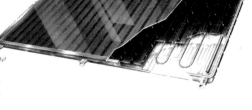

The sun's energy can be directly converted into electricity by means of the photo-electric effect. The exhibition explains the physical principles of solar cells as well as their construction, how they function and, above all, where they can be used. The conversion of solar energy into heat takes place by means of devices which either absorb, collect, or concentrate the sun's rays. They can be employed to supply hot water or to generate electricity by using a system of mirrors to concentrate the sun's energy. *sh*

△ Computer game
△ Solar collector, 1995
▽ Plasma in a glass torus

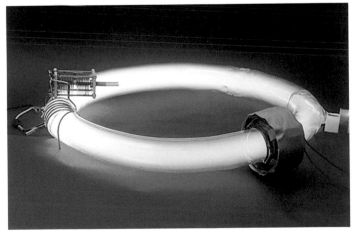

Physics is the foundation of all the natural sciences and provides the basis for the whole field of technology. It attempts to explain the laws of nature by means of experiment and theoretical deliberation. It is an exact science and expresses these relationships in mathematic formulas using precisely defined physical quantities such as force and temperature. The arrangement of the exhibition follows the path of historical development which separated physics into individual branches of knowledge. At a very early stage, mankind learned how to use mechanical devices such as the inclined plane or the pulley block, without a real understanding of the associated physical laws. The Greek word 'mechos', meaning a cunning device or a contrivance designed to 'outwit' nature, led to our words machine and mechanics, in use since the beginning of the modern age.

A series of experiments and items of original equipment illustrate the steps which led up to Galileo Galilei's formulation of the basic laws of mechanics in the early 17th century. In 1687, Isaac Newton published his *Principia Mathematica* and put forward the first unified set of rules governing mechanics. Newton's theory of classical mechanics is still applicable in almost all areas of everyday life. In the fields of twentieth century particle physics and

▷ Magdeburg hemispheres, 1663
▷ Transfer of momentum
▷ Showcase containing microscopes
▽ Early mechanical devices

cosmology, it was realised that it touched on more comprehensive theories such as quantum mechanics and the theory of relativity.

Archimedes of Syracuse, in about 250 BC, and Hero of Alexandria, in the 1st century AD, were among the first to draw important conclusions on the behaviour of liquids and gases. However, in order to formulate the physical laws which governed them, it was necessary, on the one hand, to understand the mechanics of solid bodies and, on the other, to discover that fluids and gases, just like solids, consist of atoms or molecules. Molecules of liquids, as compared with those of solid bodies, can more freely change their position relative to one another. The molecules of a gas, however, move around with almost total independence. A series of experiments on air pressure illustrates the most important discoveries.

Theoretical explanations of flowing liquids and gases are much harder to give. Their behaviour is particularly important for the design of ships and aircraft.

Oscillations and waves are common natural phenomena. In 1609, Galileo Galilei conducted scientific investigations into the oscillation of a pendulum and described the laws governing it. Numerous experiments in the exhibition depict mechanical and acoustic oscillations. The propagation of waves and the special property of intersecting wave formations which can either reinforce or cancel one another are also dealt with in a series of experiments.

Regarding the phenomenon of heat, it was recognized during the 18th century that two factors are involved: temperature and quantity of heat. Only in the nineteenth century did the idea gain acceptance that heat was produced by the random motion of the atoms or molecules of a

solid body,
liquid or gas, and could be
measured by the mean value
of this motion. Original
apparatus and several experiments trace the developments
which led at the end of the
19th century to the formulation of the law of conserva-
tion of energy.

△ Experimental apparatus used by
   Heinrich Hertz, 1887
◁ Galileo's laboratory
▽ X-ray tubes, 19th century

The first precise experiments
conducted into the phenomenon of electricity were carried
out by Henry Cavendish and
Charles Augustin de Coulomb
in the 18th century. By about
the middle of the 19th century,
numerous laws had been
discovered concerning both
static charges and electrical
current, which also produces
magnetic fields.

In 1856, James Clerk Maxwell
combined these laws into a
unified theory. Around 1888,
Heinrich Hertz confirmed
experimentally the existence
of electromagnetic radiation
such as the radio waves,
predicted by Maxwell's
equations. Moreover, light
was also recognized as a form
of electromagnetic radiation.

The section of the exhibition
dealing with electricity and
magnetism contains many
experiments and historical
examples of original apparatus
once belonging to famous
figures such as Georg Simon
Ohm, André Marie Ampère
and Heinrich Hertz. The

original vacuum tubes with
which Conrad Röntgen
discovered X-rays are also on
display.

The word 'optics' is also derived from the Greek, and means 'to do with seeing'. The first group of exhibits in the section on optics is dedicated to the physical properties of light. Experiments illustrate how light is diffused in straight lines, is reflected and refracted. The nature of light, i.e. its wave form, is demonstrated by experiments on the diffraction, interference, and polarization of light. The fact that light is also a form of (including electron microscopes and other methods of microscopy), telescopes, spectroscopic apparatus, fibre optics, interferometers and holograms, refractometers, polarimeters, and photometers. The great number of original exhibits and experiments illustrates the stages of development in the field of optics from the very beginnings to the present day.

The area of the exhibition dealing with atomic and

△ Scanning electron microscope, 1989

energy, and why there are various colours of light is also explained.

The second group of exhibits deals with vision and optics. The structure of the human eye, how it functions, and the various attempts to measure defective vision and correct it are all explained here.

The third group is made up of optical instruments. Examples of optical glass, simple optical components such as lenses and prisms and their characteristics are followed by the most important types of optical instrument: microscopes

nuclear physics explains the discovery of the atom and its nucleus as well as the laws which govern them. The introductory area traces the historic development of our understanding of the structure of matter. Original equipment and experiments outline the important steps in the discovery of radioactivity, investigations into the atomic shell and electrons, and research into the atomic nucleus. *ab*

In order to make music audible, either the human voice or an appropriate sound-producing device in the form of a musical instrument is required. Whether they are the simplest clappers or rattles used by man in prehistoric times, or the latest products of the electronics industry, all musical instruments are subject to the laws of physics and embody the technological achievements of the era in which they were built. Clearly, they have a legitimate place in a technical museum.

Musical instruments employ various methods of producing sound and are usually categorized as either percussion instruments, stringed instruments or wind instruments. The exhibition is divided up accordingly and traces the historical development of the various families of instruments in each category.

The first room contains harps, dulcimers, and related instruments. Two showcases of clavichords and spinets lead

▽ The music room

FIRST FLOOR

into the main music room. Keyboard instruments from the 16th century to the present day are exhibited here and regular concerts are given on a number of instruments, including the Thalkirchner organ (1630) in the middle of the organ loft, the romantic Steinmeyer organ opposite, the 'Bach' organ built by Jürgen Ahrend in 1995, and eight positive organs.

The harpsichord by Patavini, built in Venice in 1561, is one of the oldest quill instruments still in existence anywhere. There are several Italian and English harpsichords, clavichords by makers such as Hubert and Krämer, a virginal by Ruckers, Antwerp (1617), and numerous pianofortes from the 18th century to the present day which are also used for recitals and concerts. A low stage in the next room contains a variety of percussion instruments divided into idiophones such as rattles and bells, and membrane instruments including various kinds of drum. There are some notable examples of non-European plucked string instruments. Among the bowed stringed instruments there is a viola da gamba by Paul Alletsee (1701), a magnificent double bass by Franz Zacher (1691), the complete violin family and special forms such as the tromba marina and hurdy-gurdy. Woodwind and brass instruments are displayed opposite, including flutes, oboes,

clarinets, saxophones, cornets, horns, trumpets, and trombones. There are explanations of how these instruments are built and how they work, with particular emphasis on their valves and keys.

The section dealing with musical automata is dominated by large instruments, including an automatic organ, Hupfeld's 'Phonolizt Violina' (which consists of a piano and three violins), as well as several player pianos and a birdsong automaton.

The historically recent group of electrophones begins with the Trautonium and Theremin from the early 1930s, includes numerous electronic organs, the successful Mini-Moog and Yamaha DX7 synthesizers, and an electronic Seiler grand piano. The Siemens studio for electronic music, used by many composers in the 1960s, occupies a room of its own.

The final room is devoted to musical acoustics. Visitors can produce Chladni's sound patterns on a timpani, listen to different tuning systems on a synthesizer, experiment with resonance, or mix sounds with different overtones on a rotating disc. In the booths, it is possible to listen to computer simulations of the acoustics of famous concert halls and to call up the spectral analysis of various musical instruments. You can even analyse your own voice. *hhe*

▷ Ahrend organ, 1995
▷ Siemens sound studio, 1956

The first room in the exhibition is a replica of an alchemist's laboratory from the Middle Ages. The way the room is equipped demonstrates that alchemists also carried out experiments, although the avowed purpose of alchemy was the alchemist's own spiritual purification.

The laboratory contains hearths and various pieces of apparatus typical of the time. The art of distillation played an important role in alchemy. Equipment ranged from retorts, alembics and serpents, to a water-cooled 'Moor's head'. The earliest examples of chemical technology are a galley furnace for distilling medicinal extracts, and a 'lazy Henry', a type of oven for slow and even distillation. The second room is a replica of a chemical laboratory from the time of Antoine Lavoisier (1743-1794), who introduced quantitative methods into chemical research. It contains physical equipment such as air pumps, electrostatic generators, pneumatic troughs, and a large burning glass made by Walter Ehrenfried von Tschirnhaus around 1700.

The 18th century produced some important discoveries in the chemistry of gases and a better understanding of the processes of respiration and combustion. A niche in the rear wall of the laboratory depicts experiments carried out by Joseph Priestley and Carl Wilhelm Scheele in this area.

Perhaps the most important experiment in the history of chemistry was carried out by Lavoisier in 1789. A replica of the apparatus he used, along with his portrait, may be seen in a recess in the rear wall. By heating mercuric oxide, Lavoisier succeeded in obtaining mercury and oxygen by decomposition. These resultant elements were then allowed to react with each other, forming the oxide again. The experiment made clear the role oxygen played in the processes of oxidation and reduction, terms coined by Antoine Lavoisier, who also drew up the nomenclature still used in inorganic chemistry today.

The rise of German chemistry began with the work of Justus von Liebig (1803–1873).

△ Lavoisier's laboratory
▷ Alchemist's laboratory
▷ Experimental apparatus by Otto Hahn, Lise Meitner, and Fritz Strassmann, 1938

He was professor of chemistry in Giessen up to 1852, and then in Munich until his death. Liebig introduced practical instruction in the laboratory, completed the analysis of the elements, and propounded the theory of mineral fertilizers. The room is a replica of his laboratory in Giessen; the original can be seen in the city's Liebig Museum. Along with original instruments from his Munich laboratory, such as a laboratory stove, two Liebig condensers, a gasometer, and a Liebig drying apparatus, there are also examples of contemporary apparatus.

The glass cases at the front of the room contain preparations, scientific instruments and apparatus from the 19th century, including an equivalent slide rule, a set of blowpipes, and samples of the first aluminium and the first synthetic urea manufactured by Friedrich Wöhler (1800–1882). The large showcase on the far wall contains instruments from the estate of Eilhard Mitscherlich (1794–1863), the discoverer of isomorphism. The other half of the showcase is devoted to Robert Wilhelm Bunsen (1811–1899), who laid the foundation of spectral analysis. There are original Bunsen burners as well as adsorptiometers and an indigo prism from the scientist's estate.

The experimental part of the exhibition is divided into a number of rooms according to the important concepts used in chemistry, of which there are but a small number. These include »Matter«, »Atoms and Molecules«, »Chemical Reaction«, »Analysis and Synthesis«, and »Biochemistry«. In each section, the visitor can initiate a variety of reactions and demonstrations at the push of a button. A short text explains what is taking place.

△ Justus von Liebig's laboratory
▽ Original apparatus used by Robert Bunsen

In the section dedicated to »Matter« there is a large display containing the periodic table and samples of the elements. Groups of elements and individual elements can be made to light up via a control panel. »Atoms and Molecules« contains a showcase with the experimental apparatus used by Otto Hahn, Lise Meitner, and Fritz Strassmann to discover nuclear fission in 1938. A display tells the story of a discovery which was to change the world.

In the middle of the section on »Chemical Reactions« there is a lecture theatre. At specified times, demonstrations incorporating some impressive experiments provide visitors with an introduction to chemistry. For groups, more advanced lectures are held on subjects which often link scientific chemistry and industrial chemistry. The curator of the Chemistry department would be happy to discuss convenient dates and possible subjects. In »Analysis and Synthesis« there are more experiments

which the visitor can start at the simple push of a button as well as a number of original instruments used by Hermann Staudinger (1881-1965), the founder of macromolecular chemistry.

The section on »Biochemistry« is dominated by a large model of the DNA double helix. There is also a reconstruction of the historic pharmacy in Regensburg's St. Emmeram monastery. Here too, all the exhibits are original, once belonging to pharmacies in Munich, Regensburg, and Nuremberg. In front of the pharmacy, stands a pharmaceutical hearth of the type commonly used in the late 19th century, fitted with a water bath, distillation apparatus, and drying and sterilisation cabinets. gp

△ Experiment in the lecture theatre

△ Deoxyribonucleic acid (DNA)

▽ Pharmacy, about 1800

The exhibition begins with a survey of the base products used in the chemical industry and explains how coal, mineral oil, and water are transformed into substances for the manufacture of plastics, synthetic fibres, fertilizers, dyestuffs, and other chemical products.

A Frasch pump for the production of sulphur serves as an example of how important raw materials are obtained. The most significant industrial processes are explained by means of apparatus used for chemical reactions and models of chemical plants. Several historically interesting pieces of apparatus bear witness to the rapid development of the chemical industry.

synthesising ammonia from hydrogen and nitrogen. The next group of exhibits comprises a replica, in cross-section, of a modern ammonia combustion furnace, a slagging gas generator and a steam reforming furnace (also in cross-section) for generating hydrogen used in the synthesis of ammonia. Directly opposite this group is Karl Ziegler's pilot plant for the low-pressure synthesis of polyethylene. At the end of this section there is an original Söderberg electrode for the production of phosphorus and a model of a complete industrial plant. A model of a factory producing nitro-phosphates leads directly into the subject of the use of fertilizers, pesticides and herbicides.

The section on plastics and plastics processing gives a general survey of the ubiquity of plastics in our lives and their many uses in the modern world. Several of the machines in the exhibition are in full

Exhibits include apparatus used by Walter Reppe for investigating acetylene under pressure, and two original pilot reactors used by Matthias Pier for methanol synthesis and pressure hydrogenation of tars and heavy oils. Of special significance is the original apparatus used by Fritz Haber and Henry le Rossignol in 1908 for

be arranged for groups. In the area devoted to dyestuffs, there is a large model of the Leverkusen dye works in 1898. This was the first factory to be designed and built exclusively with production techniques in mind, and set an example for all subsequent factories in the chemical industry. Original historic samples, including synthetic ultramarine, illustrate the significance of dyestuffs in the development of the German chemical industry. The stands in the middle of the department contain experiments on various topics, and may be activated by pressing buttons. An impressive extraction column for liquid-liquid extraction

working order, and demonstrations lasting about half an hour take place several times a day. These provide an insight into some of the most important processing methods of the plastics industry. More specialized guided tours can

△ Plastics processing
◁ Haber's experimental apparatus, 1908
◁ Ziegler's apparatus, 1957
▽ Dye works Leverkusen, 1898

systems and an automatic rectifying column in continuous operation are among the final exhibits.

The final display case explains the subject of man-made fibres. Photographs and illuminated flowcharts illustrate the production, properties, and uses of the various types of synthetic fibres. *gp*

△ Potassium carbonate

▽ Production of man-made fibres

▽ Interfacial surface polymerization of nylon

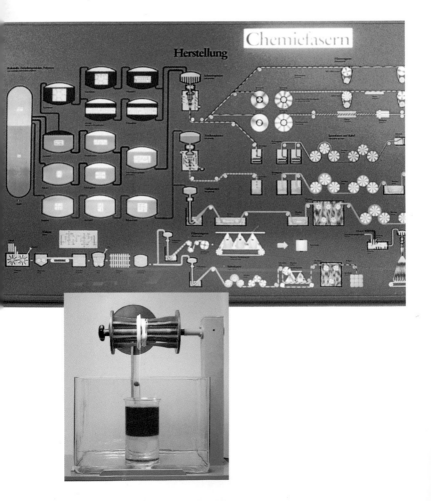

The age-old dream of human flight first became a reality in the 18th century with the invention of the hot-air balloon. The true age of aviation, however, did not begin until the 20th century, which saw the development of motorized aircraft. Aviation technology is now one of the technically and scientifically most advanced fields of industrial production.

The history of aeronautics begins over 200 years ago with the first balloon ascents, made by craft which were lighter-than-air. This subject is covered in the section »Balloons and Airships«, along the right-hand side of the old aeronautics hall. Balloon inventors all employed the principle of lift. There were two competing systems, represented by the hot-air balloons developed by the Montgolfier brothers in France, and the gas balloon invented by another Frenchman, Professor Robert Charles. The first manned ascent was made by Jacques

▷ Nosecone of the LZ 127 Zeppelin, 1928
▽ View of the old aeronautics hall
▽ The Montgolfiers, 1783

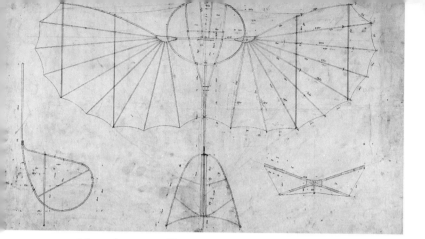

and Joseph Montgolfier from the garden of La Muette castle near Paris on 21 November 1783. This spectacular launch is faithfully reproduced in a diorama.

The direction in which balloons travelled was dependent on the wind and they did not make entirely satisfactory methods of transport. It was only towards the end of the 19th

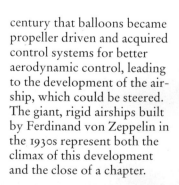

century that balloons became propeller driven and acquired control systems for better aerodynamic control, leading to the development of the airship, which could be steered. The giant, rigid airships built by Ferdinand von Zeppelin in the 1930s represent both the climax of this development and the close of a chapter.

Some idea of their sheer size can be gained from part of the nosecone of the LZ 127 *Graf Zeppelin*, which made her maiden flight in 1928 and was in service around the world for over ten years.

Long-term success, however, would belong to craft which

were heavier-than-air. These flying machines operated on the principle of dynamic lift obtained by wing surfaces placed in a moving airstream, of which nature provides many examples. The airborne movements of seeds and various animals are examined in the section »Flight in Nature«, along the left-hand side of the old aeronautics hall. For centuries, unsuccessful attempts were made to imitate the flight of birds. The first man to design a suitable gliding device, and to learn to fly, was Otto Lilienthal. He made the first successful

◁ Lilienthal's standard wing glider, 1894
◁ Lilienthal in one of his gliders, 1893
▽ Wright brothers' Standard Type A, 1909
▽ World War I fighter Fokker D VIII, 1918

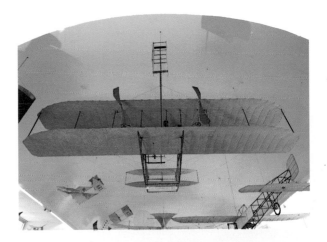

flight just outside Berlin in 1891. In the following years he built several more flying machines. Replicas of Lilienthal's 'standard' wing glider and his double-winged glider, with its dummy pilot in typical flying position, are suspended from the ceiling at the end of the old aeronautics hall, near the section »The Early Days of Flight«. Lilienthal's flights were the result of many years of careful study, calculation, and experiments. He made over 2000 flights, and had been airborne for over two hours before his fatal crash in 1896. Based on Lilienthal's publications and their own experiments, the Americans Orville and Wilbur Wright succeeded, in 1903, in making the first powered flight. Their aircraft was equipped with a specially designed Otto engine and could be controlled around all three axes. In 1908/09 the Wright brothers demonstrated a series-production aircraft in Europe too. Developed from their original Flyer, it boosted aircraft development on this side of the Atlantic. The only surviving example of the Standard Type A series (1909) is also suspended from the ceiling of the old aeronautics hall.

The military significance of aircraft was recognized at an early stage. Even before World War I, military requirements and tenders began to influence aircraft design, leading to the manufacture of sturdy,

production-line models. Between 1914 and 1918, increasingly large numbers of aircraft were built for use by the rapidly growing air forces as reconnaissance planes, bombers and fighter aircraft. The Fokker D VII is a typical fighter plane of the period. Aircraft design placed huge demands on technology, and science played an important role in their construction. The section »Aerodynamics and Mechanics of Flight«, situated in the passageway leading to the new aeronautics hall, includes replicas of the facilities used by Lilienthal and the Wright brothers for aerodynamic experiments. There is also a demonstration showing the pressure distribution on an aircraft wing in a wind tunnel. After World War I, a more peaceful use was found for the aircraft: as a means of transport, it underwent considerable development, using stronger materials, becoming larger and more reliable. The first successful commercial aircraft was the Junkers F 13, which made its maiden flight in 1919. One of the few restored originals can be seen on the first floor of the new hall. Influenced by the designs of luxury limousines, it held four passengers and a crew of two.

The enclosed cabin and all-metal construction pointed the way for future aircraft manufacture. The F 13 was used throughout the world for freight transportation and in civil aviation.

The three-engined Junkers Ju 52 was developed from the F 13 and came onto the market in 1932. It was the standard passenger aircraft used by Deutsche Lufthansa in the 1930s. During World War II, thousands of these planes were manufactured and used as transport aircraft. Inside the Ju 52 cockpit, visitors can examine some of the most advanced

instrumentation of the day. Since the 1920s, aircraft had become increasingly equipped with instruments such as the artificial horizon designed for 'blind' flying and to help the pilot maintain course under conditions of poor visibility. The exhibition »Flight Control and Navigation« is to be found in the lower mezzanine gallery. The simultaneous demand

◁ »Flight in Nature«: a seed pod
△ Wind-tunnel experiment
▽ General view of the new
   aeronautics hall

for smaller planes suitable for sporting, touring, and training purposes, led to the development of mostly single-seater and two-seater aircraft. Originally, they used lightweight wooden designs, but later were often all-metal constructions. During the 1920s, and before the days of regular air traffic, light aircraft such as the Klemm 25 and Junkers Junior in the display were often flown on 'pioneer' and long-haul flights in order to demonstrate the capabilities of the new technology.

Increasing political tension in the 1930s brought about massive investment in armaments and the development of a much larger airforce. With the use of aircraft, war acquired a terrifying new dimension. Bombers caused previously unimaginable destruction by

The Messerschmitt Bf 109 E fighter aircraft (1938) in the eastern part of the new hall represents a new generation of combat aircraft. It uses a light, stressed-skin monocoque construction, aerodynamic design and high-power engine. The Bf 109 entered series production during World War II and was used by the German Luftwaffe as its standard fighter.

The development of small, light, powerful and reliable forms of propulsion played a vital role in the performance of aircraft. Otto engines were used by the first airships and aircraft as a propulsion method. The special demands on aircraft construction led to innovative designs such as the radial engine. The section »Piston Engines« contains an

carrying out saturation bombing; even the Ju 52 was refitted for this purpose from time to time.

early rotary engine, the Oberursel UO, built in 1914 and shown here in cross-section.

Other special topics in the history of aviation are dealt with in more detail in the upper mezzanine gallery. There are exhibits on »Aviation Safety and Rescue«, and »Model Aeroplane Technology«. The central area of the new aeronautics hall is dedicated to an exciting era in aviation history: that of the jet aircraft. The jet engine was the result of efforts to increase the speed of an aircraft beyond the technical limits of the propeller, which lie between 700 and 800 kph. The jet engine does

not have this type of limitation. Its development took

place against an ominous background, however. In 1939, the first aircraft with jet propulsion, a Heinkel He 178, was successfully tested.

◁ Commercial aircraft Junkers F 13, 1919
∧ Klemm Kl 25 light aircraft, 1935
▷ Cockpit of the Boeing 707, 1959
▽ Fighter aircraft Messerschmitt Me 109, 1938

Shortly afterwards, the Second World War broke out. A replica of the Heinkel He S3B turbojet engine developed by Hans von Ohain is on display. Towards the end of World War II, the jet engine was developed for series production and was used in fighter aircraft. The first jet aircraft to be produced in quantity was the two-engined Messerschmitt Me 262. Experiments with rocket-propelled aircraft were also

carried out during the last war. In 1943, the Messerschmitt Me 163 was fitted with rocket propulsion and intended for use as a high performance interceptor aircraft.

After the war, jet aircraft underwent further development and were used throughout the world for military purposes and in civil aviation. It did not take long before these aircraft, especially the military jets, could exceed the speed of sound. The American Lockheed F-104 *Starfighter* was the fastest fighter of its day, and was capable of reaching Mach 2.

It was also used by the German Luftwaffe, but the frequent crashes due to its somewhat under-developed technical system soon gained it a bad reputation.

In order to obviate the need for long runways used during take-off and landing, VTOL (vertical take off and landing) jets were developed in the 1960s. The VJ 101 C, a vertical take-off fighter, was developed and produced by a team of designers at Munich's Entwicklungsring Süd.

The future of the jet aircraft lay, however, in the development of wide-bodied jets used for cargo and passenger transport. The A300 Airbus is a perfect example of this trend in Europe. The parts on display are all original and come from the Airbus Prototype I. They illustrate the construction methods used, as well as the scale and technical specifications of such an aircraft and the typical fanjet engine developed for it, the CF6 built by General Electric in 1971. On the ground floor, jet aircraft and jet engines are displayed, as well as helicopters, gliders, and the European SPACELAB.

The helicopter, with its vertical take-off and landing capability, was developed in the 1930s for special operations. The first helicopter which was fit to fly and developed beyond the experimental stage was the Focke-Wulf Fw 61 (1936). A test model can be seen in the showcase along with exhibits on the early history of the helicopter.

The Sikorsky S-55 (1949), with its complex rotor system, belongs to the first generation of series-produced helicopters. Lightweight turbo-shaft engines supplanted piston engines in the 1960s. Rotor blades made of glass-fibre reinforced plastic, such as those used on the Bölkow 105 built by MBB in 1969, made possible the construction of a hingeless rotor system with good maintenance ability.

Gliding has had an important influence on German aviation development. The first gliders were based on Lilienthal's gliding devices and produced in the early 1920s, at a time when powered flight in Germany was still forbidden under terms imposed after the war had been lost.

The *Vampyr* (1921) was the first glider to stay aloft for several hours. Its design principles set the standard for the next decades.

A new developmental phase began at the end of the 1950s with the fs 24 *Phönix* built by the Stuttgart Academic Flying Group and the introduction of fibre reinforced plastics in combination with laminar wing sections in glider construction.

Just outside the new aeronautics hall is the *Würzburg Riese*, a giant radar tracking antenna from World War II.

The Oberschleissheim branch of the Deutsches Museum contains several more exhibits on aeronautics and astronautics (see back cover). *gf, bg, wh, hho*

◁ Ejection seat in operation, 1967
◁ Oberursel UO rotary engine, 1914
▽ View of the new aviation hall

The second floor is arranged around the four sides of a square and it is quite difficult to get lost. By following the route which has been marked out, the fascinating history of European crafts unfolds. From ceramics and glass making, and printing and papermaking, to spinning and weaving, the story is remarkable and intriguing.

Not surprisingly, all these manual crafts ended up as industrial processes. Mechanical looms used in the manufacture of textiles and steam powered machinery lent a great impetus to the industrial revolution. The Jacquard loom, which was controlled by punch-cards, is actually one of the ancestors of the computer.

The second floor also houses an additional room for special exhibitions and two smaller sections devoted to special forms of handicrafts: the

SECOND FLOOR

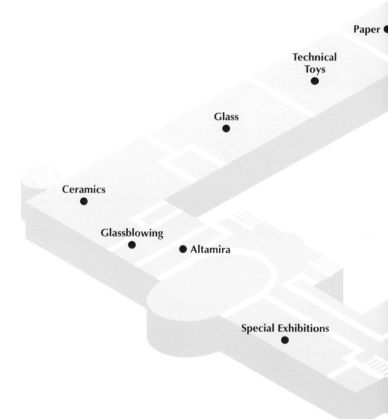

Department of Technical Toys and the Altamira Cave. Altamira is a hill in north-east Spain where a cave was discovered containing paintings made over 14 000 years ago. On the cave roof, the numerous depictions of animals are among the earliest and finest examples of paleolithic art. The Deutsches Museum used radical new techniques to achieve an exact replica of the paintings and the ceiling of the cave itself. A new department dealing with Stone Age Technology is currently being planned.

Overleaf is a description of the Astronautics department, which can be reached via the Department of Aeronautics.

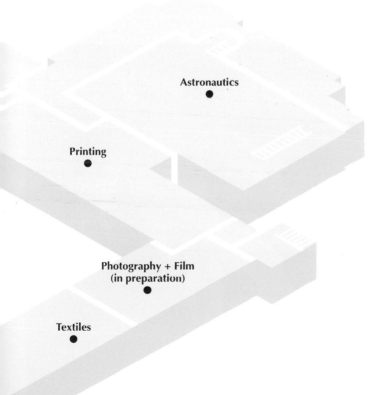

Astronautics

Printing

Photography + Film
(in preparation)

Textiles

The term 'astronautics' describes the technical means by which vehicles or machines may be sent into space. This is one of the few branches of technology where we can state a precise date when science fiction became science fact. On 4 October 1957, Russian engineers succeeded for the first time in putting an artificial satellite into a stable orbit round the earth.

At least 3000 years ago, man

tifically. In 1923, Hermann Oberth's book *By Rocket into Interplanetary Space* showed that it was a feasible technical proposition. Unfortunately, the history of the space rocket then became inextricably linked to the development of weapons technology. During World War II, German scientists at

▷ HELIOS space probe, 1974
▷ A4 rocket (V2), 1945
▷ Max Valier's rocket car, 1930
▽ American space suit, 1965

had already begun to wonder about the significance of the heavens. It was only in the twentieth century, however, that the possibility of space flight was investigated scien-

the army's rocket facility at Peenemünde on the Baltic coast developed the first large liquid-propellant rockets. Many people lost their lives building the so-called V2

rocket and as a result of its use. After the war, it was mainly the USA and the former Soviet Union who made use of German know-how and built intercontinental missiles armed with atomic warheads. Although the rockets themselves could also be used for peaceful purposes, space flight offered such prestigious opportunities for technological development that it became dominated by the ensuing cold war between East and West. It did not take long to discover the possibilities afforded by this new science: meteorological satellites could monitor the earth's weather patterns from space and telecommunication satellites made possible the rapid transmission of radio signals and television pictures around the world. Space probes have revolutionized our knowledge of the solar system. Today, space flight is almost part of everyday life. The darkened room at the beginning of the exhibition deals with ideas about the cosmos in ancient times and the transition from a visionary and utopian cosmogony to one based on scientific reality. A replica spacesuit reminds us of the historic space walk by Edward White on 10 June 1965, as part of the GEMINI 4 flight. Three demonstrations at the

▽ AZUR space probe, 1969
▽ APOLLO 15 on the moon

beginning of this section illustrate Newton's principle that »for every action there is an equal and opposite reaction.« The rocket-driven sled and car built by Max Valier in 1929 are rare and extremely valuable exhibits from the pioneering days of rocket development.

There is a replica of the liquid-propellant rocket built in 1926 by the American Robert Goddard, which made the first successful flight, as well as the first liquid-propellant rocket to be launched in Europe, built by Johannes Winkler in 1931. A technical breakthrough in the development of this type of rocket was achieved with the construction of the A4 rocket. It was developed at the secret rocket facility in Peenemünde as a remote-controlled weapon designed to support the war effort and nicknamed V2 by the Nazis. An A4 rocket motor has been cut away to show how the new technology worked, and a complete A4 stands next to the spiral staircase; both exhibits date from 1945.

Both the Russians and the Americans made important advances in liquid-propellant rockets after the war. Examples of American rocket motors are the H1 (1959) and the J2 (1964) which powered the famous Saturn rockets. In Germany, research into space flight was forbidden

until the end of the 1950s. The beginning of the German aerospace industry is marked by the construction of the third stage of the EUROPA rocket in 1971, under the auspices of Ludwig Bölkow. Today, the European nations cooperate in building the ARIANE rocket launcher. The two Ariane rocket motors on display are the HM-7 (1982) and the VIKING (1979). The principle of electric propulsion occupies a special position in the development of rocket motors. Electric rocket motors can usually only operate in a vacuum and provide a relatively low thrust. In a specially darkened room a plasma motor, which uses argon

gas, may be seen in operation. A series of models of launch vehicles built to a scale of 1:25 depict developments in the USA, the former USSR, and Europe. In 1961, the Russian Yuri Gagarin was the first

man in space. A replica of the MERCURY capsule, in which the American John Glenn orbited the earth not long afterwards, illustrates the early stages of manned space flight. In order to protect astronauts from an extremely hostile environment, space suits are worn during the more dangerous phases of a space flight. Space suits worn by F. Bormann on the GEMINI 7 flight and D. Eisele on the APOLLO 7 mission are on display. In 1969, the Americans landed the first men on the moon, an enormous financial undertaking which called for a supreme effort by those involved. A large diorama depicts a scene from the APOLLO-15 mission, which made the fourth successful American moon landing. Numerous pieces of equipment give an idea of the extensive programme of scientific experiments which the astronauts carried out. A small piece of moon rock shielded by armoured glass reminds us of the largest space exploration programme to date. After these moon landings, the Americans concentrated on developing a reusable space craft: the space shuttle. A scale model (1:25) shows the shuttle with the SPACELAB, which was developed in Germany. An original SPACELAB may be seen on the ground floor of the Aeronautics hall. This piece of equipment was not actually sent into space, but was subjected to an extensive series of tests carried out by

△ Terrestrial receiving station for
   meteorological data
△ METEOSAT picture
◁ SPACELAB, 1983

MBB-ERNO in Bremen to determine operational and functional reliability.

It is not the manned missions which have made astronautics an indispensable part of modern life, but the many satellites and space probes. A receiving station for pictures gathered by meteorological satellites demonstrates how information about the weather is transmitted from space, something we appear to take for granted. Along with pictures from METEOSAT, in geostationary orbit over Europe, it is also possible to receive images taken by American NOAA meteorological satellites which are in low polar orbit. Special demonstrations explore in depth the possibilities of exploiting data received by meteorological satellites. A further demonstration explains the unusual qualities of the orbits of geostationary satellites. The first space probes to be built in

Germany were AZUR and AEROS, designed to gather scientific data about that part of space in closest proximity to the earth. For the first time, German research institutes were able to carry out unaided a complete space project. The new space flight technology offered scientists previously undreamed of possibilities to study the sun and the solar system. An impressive example is the solar probe HELIOS, built in Germany in 1974. Two probes of this type are still in orbit around the sun. They are the first objects to have sent back detailed data from the vicinity of our nearest star. The MOMS-01 satellite camera provides high-resolution pictures of the earth's surface. It can distinguish details only 15 m in size and flew on several space shuttle missions. In the showcase is an experimental piece of equipment from which test pictures could be developed. It was used on board an aircraft and contains a small semiconductor chip which actually took the pictures. *mk*

In 1879, a cave containing stone-age paintings was discovered at Altamira in northern Spain. The exhibition contains a replica of the cave roof. Today, the Altamira cave is no longer open to the public. The cave paintings were made nearly 15 000 years ago in the late paleolithic period. They depict animals which lived during the ice age. Apart from a horse and several 'hind' or female deer, mainly bison can be seen, along with a number of abstract figures. The paintings were made using natural pigments such as yellow, red and brownish ochres as well as black manganese earth and charcoal. In places, they are engraved into the rock. For the bison in particular, the colours are gradated into such a vast array of shades that the creatures appear three-dimensional and amazingly realistic. The bison which are lying down are painted on naturally occurring folds in the rock and function as both paintings and reliefs.

In front of the entrance, there is a general introduction to the various epochs of the Stone Age, its art and particularly its cave paintings.

The actual Altamira cave is entered through an air lock placed in the cave entrance. This protects it from daylight, traps the cold air and maintains the constant low temperature and high humidity which have successfully preserved the ancient paintings up to now. The exhibition contains descriptions of the complicated processes evolved by the Deutsches Museum for reproducing an exact copy of the original roof in terms of shape and the materials used. The department now plans to mount a more detailed exhibition dedicated to the technology of the Stone Age. It will illustrate the cultural and technical achievements of the period, including the invention and gradual refinement of tools, the discovery of fire, and the era's manifold means of artistic expression. The agrarian revolution in the Neolithic Age saw the introduction of organized farming methods and the beginnings of a more sedentary existence. This led to a number of inventions and discoveries, such as ceramics, weaving, the wheel, writing, and the smelting of bronze, which provided the basis for today's technology, culture and civilization. *mb*

◁ Cave painting, detail of roof
▷ Cave painting, general view

Ceramics are the oldest artificial materials known to mankind and are some ten thousand years old. The earliest earthenware vessels were used to store food and for cooking. The raw material from which they were manufactured was clay, which could be found almost everywhere. By the time of Christ, ceramics were known in nearly all parts of the world. Important milestones on the way to the manufacture of modern ceramics were the invention of the potter's wheel in the middle of the 4th millennium BC, the introduction of stoneware about the same time, and the production of porcelain in China in about the 7th century AD. Clay was used to make not only receptacles, but also bricks, tiles, and water pipes. The exhibition is divided into four distinct sections. »Ceramics in Antiquity« displays a selection of early earthenware vessels and jars, bricks and pipes. It also deals with the invention of the potter's wheel

and the subsequent widespread use of ceramics in the ancient world.

The second room, »Classical Ceramic Commodities«, is devoted to earthenware, stoneware, whiteware and porcelain. Various pots and jars, floor tiles and wall tiles, bricks, and a tiled oven are a rich source of contemporary evidence. A short survey summarizes the historic development of these materials.

△ Apostle mug, 1692

▽ Ancient storage and transport vessels

»Technical Ceramics«, the third area of the exhibition, traces the development of the industrial uses of ceramics, which began in the mid-19th century. Their properties of heat resistance and resistance to chemical corrosion are illustrated by a series of examples. equipment, machinery, and models illustrating the stages of preparation, forming, and firing of ceramics. Finally, there is a fully automatic, small-scale model of a brickmaking plant, which produces miniature bricks for visitors. *gk*

Another important characteristic of ceramics is their high electrical resistance, necessary for materials used in high-voltage insulators and spark plugs. Along with traditional clay materials, more and more ceramic products are made of synthetic raw materials. Ceramic materials of this type have many uses, such as substrates for electronic circuits, abrasive parts for grinding machines, cutting tools and wear-resistant machine tools, capacitors and semiconductors, and as magnets in electric motors. The final room, »Manufacture of Ceramic Products«, displays

△ Brickmaking plant
▽ Industrial ceramics

Glass consists mainly of quartz, also known as silicon dioxide or SiO$_2$. At temperatures of over 1700° C, this substance becomes molten and can be shaped. With the addition of fluxes such as soda or potash, a melting point of about 1000° C can be achieved. Lime adds strength to the molecular structure. Glass is one of the

oldest artificial raw materials. Glass ornaments were already in use about 6000 BC, in Mesopotamian times. Around 1350 BC, the Egyptians produced the first glass vessels by wrapping filaments of molten glass around a mould made of sand. The basic principle of forming glass by blowing was discovered in about 200 BC by the Syrians, who were able to achieve higher temperatures and invented the glassblower's pipe. Originally an

expensive luxury, glass is now part of everyday life, used for bottles, drinking glasses, window panes and optical lenses. The four sections of the exhibition are devoted to glass as a material, hollow ware, flat glass, and specialized glass. »Material: Glass« explains the composition and properties of glass. Models show how glass was melted in former times and explain today's industrial production techniques. The subjects of energy and the environment are also addressed.

»Hollow Ware« deals with traditional methods of manufacture in glassworks and the important stages in the gradual automation of glassmaking, right up to modern glass-blowing machines which can produce 450 bottles a minute. The rich and varied ways in which craftsmen decorated containerware are illustrated by examples of glass which have been painted or coloured by overlay, engraved, embossed, and etched.

In »Flat Glass«, the production of windows and mirrors is explained. This section also traces a historical path and describes the skills used in the manufacture of crown glass and blown sheet glass for window panes. Mirrors are punched out of founded sheet glass. Modern industrial production techniques use inexpensive float glass for windows and mirrors alike. Earlier, only mirrors were coated with amalgam or silver. Today, this is a standard process applied to glass used for cars and buildings. Various exhibits and experiments demonstrate the use of laminated glass for car windscreens and bullet-proof glass, as well as the uses of heatproof, fireproof and soundproof glass. Historically speaking, the section »Specialized Glass« begins with the figure of Otto Schott who, between 1876 and 1884, worked with Ernst Abbe

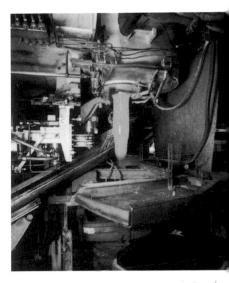

△ Cathode ray tube press, 1988
◁ A cage cup, or diatretum
◁ Glassworks in Zwiesel, about 1950
▽ Bulletproof glass after impact
of a projectile

on the development of special compounds and methods for manufacturing the type of optical glass needed for telescopes, microscopes and for optical fibres used today. Experiments illustrate the special properties of such glass, including its optical qualities and its resistance to acids and alkalis, heat, or sudden changes in temperature. Glass fibres are also made from special glass and are used today as textile glass, especially to reinforce synthetic materials, or as glass wool used for insulation. The production methods involved are also explained. Glass-blowing demonstrations are held daily – currently next to the entrance to the Altamira cave. Visitors can watch how glass tubes and rods are heated in the flame of a gas burner, known as a 'lamp' and, as they begin to melt, are blown and worked into various shapes. *mb*

This department is not primarily concerned with scientific and technical topics. It deals instead with the history of technical construction kits, the opportunity they afford for play, and their ability to recreate the architectural and technological environment. They demonstrate in an exemplary way the relationship between technology, architecture, and games. In the middle of the 'market place', there is a monument to the renowned educationalist Friedrich Fröbel, the father of the construction kit. The four main rooms leading off from the square contain examples of construction kits made of wood, stone, metal, and plastic. The section »Wooden Construction Kits« contains building blocks on particular

subjects, such as the set of *Münchner Kindl* building bricks and sets of blocks from the Erz mountains. These sets of elementary building blocks, which give children complete freedom of design and construction, were recognised early on as valuable toys in kindergartens. More sophisticated sets were soon developed, such as Dusyma and Matador, which allowed the blocks to be fastened together. »Stone Construction Kits« is dedicated to the Anker bricks.

Their colour schemes made it possible to build more realistic structures. These sets of bricks also accurately reflect social and cultural history, whether they were used to build palaces, simple cottages, bridges or fortresses. »Metal Construction Kits« were invented by Frank Hornby in the early 20th century. They are much closer to the actual technology they were designed to represent. There are examples of all kinds of vehicle, from those with geared transmissions, to cranes and excavators, as well as a Ferris wheel and an aircraft, all built from the classic Meccano, Märklin, Stabil, and Trix construction kits. The exhibition contains a comprehensive collection of sets from the post-war years. »Plastic Construction Kits« are relative newcomers. The first type to appear was Idema, closely followed by Lego and Fischertechnik. These toys are no longer mere building blocks, but sophisticated, miniature engineering systems which, in the case of the Fischer kits, allow the simulation of technical processes in the form of an industrial model. *gk*

△ Märklin steamroller, 1965
◁ »Münchner Kindl« church, 1904
◁ Anker church, about 1880
▽ Entrance to the exhibition

Paper is a thin mat of cellulose fibres of vegetable origin. The coherence of the fibres is achieved both mechanically, by matting, and chemically, with hydrogen bonds. It can have a greater tensile strength than steel. The forerunners of paper were papyrus, parchment and tapa. These materials and the age of hand-made paper are the main topics of the first section of the exhibition. A Japanese papermaking workshop illustrates the beginnings of paper manufacturing in East Asia.

European papermaking only began in the 13th century and is characterised by equipment such as the rag shredder, stamping mill, Hollander beating mill, screw press and laid mould. There are daily demonstrations of the hand scooping process. In a darkened room there are examples of old paper containing watermarks, and other documents on the history of papermaking. The second part of the exhibition covers the beginnings of industrial paper manufacture. In 1798/99, Louis-Nicolas Robert invented the endless screen papermaking machine. The principle of the endless web was subsequently used by all modern papermaking machines. The department's most valuable exhibit is a French endless screen papermaking machine from about 1820, the oldest machine of this kind still in existence. In the 1840s, wood pulp

△ Papermaking in Japan, about 1900
▷ Endless screen papermaking
 machine, 1956
▽ Papermaking machine,
 France, 1820

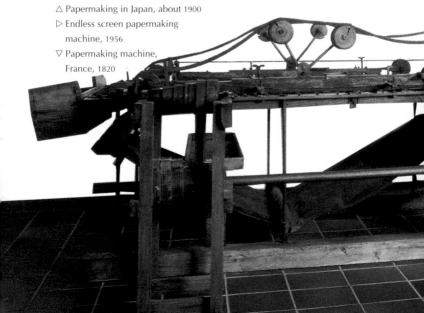

replaced rags as the raw material for paper. Another unique exhibit is a small piece of equipment built by Gottfried Keller in 1843: his manual wood pulping machine. A cardboard-making machine, dating from 1910, illustrates the importance of the manufacture of cardboard containers. The sheer size of the machinery used in modern papermaking, the subject of the final room, means that it can only be demonstrated in the form of models. The working model of a modern papermaking machine is demonstrated several times a week. The low speed of about 2 m per minute allows observation of the formation of the paper web on the screen and its passage through the press and dryer sections. The need to test the quality of paper and to standardize the various grades arose in the late 19th century. A collection of testing equipment is evidence of the importance of this field. The final exhibit, an 'A to Z of Papermaking', includes about 80 different grades of paper, card and cardboard. *wg*

SECOND FLOOR

Between about 1440 and 1450, Johannes Gensfleisch Gutenberg invented letterpress printing, a method of duplicating large numbers of identical prints at low cost. This was the technical prerequisite which made books accessible to a larger audience, accounted for the rise of newspapers and periodicals, and generally brought about a much wider dissemination of the written word than ever before. Hardly any other invention has exercised such a great influence on civilization and society.

The first room, covering manual printing, contains examples of various types of script and writing implements. There are regular demonstrations of composition with movable metal type. The techniques of printing pictures from woodcuts and copper engravings also date back to the era of Gutenberg. Simple hand presses were in use from the 15th to the 19th century. The four on display are late examples of this type of press. The craft of bookbinding is illustrated by a diorama,

various tools, and samples of binding. Two large dioramas at the end of the room illustrate how Gutenberg's invention revolutionized communication. A monk copying texts in a scriptorium makes a dramatic contrast with the printing works of about 1800.

A facsimile of the famous Gutenberg bible is displayed between these two exhibits. The second room is devoted to the machine age. In the 19th century, printing underwent a technological revolution, brought about by the new typesetting machines which allowed mechanical composition of the text. The Linotype machine invented by Ottmar Mergenthaler in 1883 and Talbot Lanston's Monotype machine, built in 1965, can both be demonstrated. They indicate how printing was carried out before the advent of photo-typesetting in the 1970s.

◁ Meisenbach half-tone print
▷ Iron lever press, 1826
▷ Wooden screw press, 1790

The reproduction of pictures also changed dramatically. Between 1796 and 1798, Alois Senefelder invented lithography, a completely new printing method which used prepared limestone. The first pole press, a portable press, and various tools from his workshop are all on display. Senefelder's invention of the first planographic or offset printing method led to chromolithography, and allowed the first realistic colour prints to be produced. Between 1882 and 1889, Georg Meisenbach developed a method of decomposing pictures into a matrix of halftone dots which could be transferred to zinc plates. Among the exhibits are a halftone plate, an early process camera (1925), and the first machine for etching the plate. The next section contains various machines for making plates used to print banknotes and securities. Much space is devoted to printing machines – the oldest surviving high-speed press and the oldest sheet-fed gravure press are both displayed. A rotary press for printing newspapers and two high-speed rotary presses (one for newspapers, the other for printing two colours in one run) can be demonstrated. Several original bookbinding machines, a model of a steam operated book bindery, and various examples of bookbinding are also on display.

The final room is dedicated to modern printing techniques. The introduction of electronic processing of text and illustrations led to a second revolution in the printing industry. Phototypesetting replaced

SECOND FLOOR

material, as well as on curved surfaces. Two monochrome offset machines are displayed at the end of the series of printing machines.

Modern bookbinding is illustrated by the model of an adhesive binder line, a high-speed cutter, various machine parts, and samples of binding. A bookshop acts as a reminder of how the printed word is actually disseminated. Several computer stations throughout the exhibition offer explanations of important machinery and products and more detailed information on some of the many aspects of printing technology. *wg*

the old hot-metal machines in the 1970s. Text either takes the form of a photographic negative or is stored as digitally encoded information. Pictures are scanned electronically by scanners. High-performance minicomputers process the text and images using appropriate software, produce the final layout, and output the results via negative face carriers onto photographic film. The Digiset exhibited here was the first machine capable of copying letters stored in binary code onto film via a cathode-ray tube.

The main exhibit is a fully operational desk-top publishing (DTP) system. Screen printing is a special method used to print on practically all types of

◁ Senefelder's pole press, 1797
▽ Linotype 6c Quick, 1965

The dawn of modern visual communications was characterised by the invention of photography and film. The exhibition, currently being redesigned and intended to open in 1997, spans the early pioneering era through to today's electronic images. The first section is devoted to the technical aspects of creating a photographic image, including the chemical processing of the exposed film.

△ Daguerre camera, 1839
▽ All-metal Voigtländer, 1841

The interactive displays placed throughout the exhibition provide information on the optical principles of photography, explain how exposure times are calculated and distances are measured, and deal with the characteristics of different types of film and their developing processes. Various camera components illustrate improvements in camera design and the light sensitive material used. The centrepiece of the exhibition, placed in front of an architectural model, is a studio camera with lens carriers adjusted by an electric motor. Some exhibits, especially from the early days, are unique in Germany. Daguerre's original camera (1839) is displayed, as is an all-metal

Voigtländer camera (1841), together with the complete equipment necessary to produce daguerreotypes. A series of photographs from various ages illustrates how the technical

achievements of a particular era influenced the image created. The introduction of electronic components in cameras, and digital imaging techniques are the final topics of this section.

The use of photography in scientific research is a relatively little known field. Microphotography, high-speed photography, and infra-red and ultra-violet photography help us access a normally invisible and fascinating world. Here too, interactive demonstrations are used to explain these subjects. The final section deals with the history of the moving image, from the subtle art of the laterna magica and an early motion picture camera designed to take 'instantaneous shots in sequence', to professional and amateur cinematographic equipment.

The advent of the 'talking picture' and the introduction of colour film are dealt with in separate sections. There is also a life-size replica of a film set with state of the art equipment. Video projection and sound-and-slide shows using various dissolving techniques are demonstrated in the projection room. *ck*

▽ 35 mm cameras
▽ Cinematographic projector
   Panzerkino, 1912
▽ Stroboscope, 1933/34

As human civilization developed, clothing began to play an increasingly significant role. Garments were worn in many early cultures for a variety of reasons. They offered protection against the climate, performed a decorative function and acted as a mark of social distinction. Clothing rapidly became as important as food and shelter.

The exhibition outlines the history of textile manufacture from the Stone Age to the industrial revolution of the 18th century and on into the present day. Authentic recreations of historical scenes and the department's own textile factory provide an insight into textile production down through the ages. Early examples of textile machines and modern computer-controlled machinery complete the picture.

Five scenes illustrate these developments:

– Domestic spinning and weaving in the Stone Age, about 4000 BC
– The use of slave labour for highly skilled textile manufacturing in Ancient Egypt, about 2000 BC
– The monotony of a textile workshop, about 1728, and the beginnings of specialized manual skills as a means of increasing productivity
– Cottage industry and the piece-work system in the 18th and 19th centuries
– Mechanical cotton spinning

◁ Hand loom with 'flying shuttle', 1733
▽ Experimental work bench

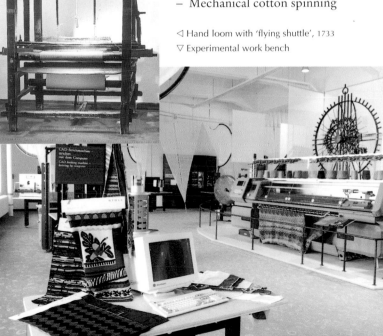

and weaving in Augsburg around 1840 and the beginnings of the machine age in Bavaria.

The rapid change-over from manual labour to mechanical production during the 18th and 19th centuries is known as the 'textile revolution'. The factory in the centre of the exhibition highlights these far-reaching developments. Important historic illustrations include the world's first textile factory, built at Cromford mill in England in 1771, and the first textile factory in continental Europe, Cromford Ratingen, which dates from 1784. Faithful replicas of the machines used in Richard Arkwright's 'factory system' may also be seen. Historical and modern machines are juxtaposed for comparison. A spinning wheel and flyer spinning frame, the famous 'spinning Jenny', the revolutionary hand loom with a 'flying shuttle', a manual Jacquard loom with punch-card system, a 400-year-old frame loom for making stockings, and a dilapidated perrotine fabric printing machine compete for space with a rotor spinning machine, computerized air-jet loom, flat-bed knitting machine with CAD system, and the latest dyeing equipment. All the machines are in full working order and can be demonstrated. The exhibition also gives an account of their origins, use, function, production capacity and historical

importance. Working conditions varied considerably throughout the history of textile manufacture and are illustrated by a series of large colour photographs placed above the machines.

The department's factory is itself surrounded by experimental work-benches where visitors can satisfy their curiosity about the underlying principles of textile manufacturing, using interactive displays. Fibres can be twisted into a thread, a shed can be formed on a loom, and a tubular fabric knitted. The properties of microfibres, non-woven fabrics and other technical textiles can also be studied.

Interactive displays explain the subjects of »Fibrous Materials«, »Manufacture of Felt and Bonded Fabrics«, and »Textile Finishing«. Two dioramas demonstrate the importance of the final stage of manufacture: finishing. This process renders fabrics attractive, wear-resistant, and easier to care for.

An interactive display provides the answers to specialized questions. *ht*

△ Textile manufacture in a mill, about 1840
△ Interactive display
◁ General view of the exhibition

The third floor, like the second, forms a neat square. This world of precision engineering and high technology includes chronometers and scales, the fields of geodesy (surveying and mapping), computers, microelectronics, and telecommunications. Some time should be spent viewing the historic mathematical instruments and calculating devices, as there is much interesting information to read. The wonderful collection of Brüggemann clocks is also hard to leave.

At first sight, the Agriculture department does not seem to have any connection with present day technology. The juxtaposition of ancient and modern is intentional, however, and the opportunity should not be missed to ponder on the rapid changes in lifestyle witnessed this century.

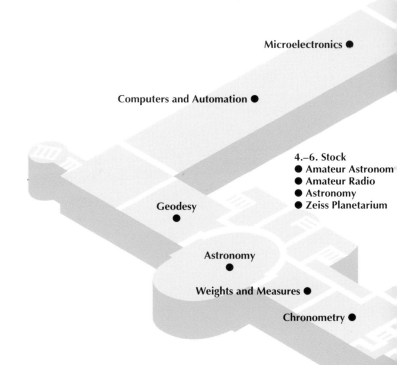

Microelectronics ●

Computers and Automation ●

4.–6. Stock
● Amateur Astronom
● Amateur Radio
● Astronomy
● Zeiss Planetarium

Geodesy
●

Astronomy
●

Weights and Measures ●

Chronometry ●

The layout of the Department of Astronomy needs a little explanation. The best place to begin is the section on models of the universe and the motion of the stars. By climbing the stairs to the gallery, the telescopes and satellites can then be viewed. From here, the departments of Amateur Astronomy and Amateur Radio on the fourth floor can be reached. A spiral staircase leads to the fifth floor and the sections devoted to the sun, moon, planets, and cosmology. The sixth floor houses the Zeiss Planetarium, not to be confused with the planetarium in the 'Forum der Technik' building, and admission tickets should be obtained early, from the information desk on the ground floor. The roof of the museum offers a rewarding view over Munich, its environs and, on especially clear days, the Alps themselves.

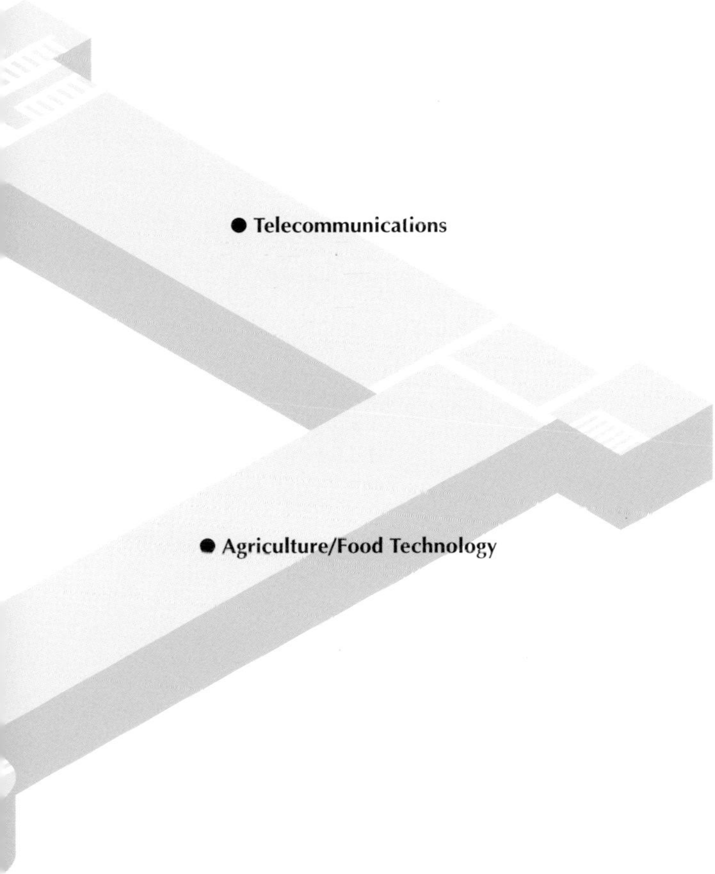

● Telecommunications

● Agriculture/Food Technology

Geodesy is the science of measuring the size and shape of the earth, making a survey of its surface features,

'gravimetry', or the measurement of gravity. There is also an explanation of aerial photogrammetry and satellite geodesy.

Geodesy comprises a number of individual disciplines. These include measuring the size and shape of the earth, determining the topography, applying geodetic procedures to engineering surveying and performing 'cadastral' surveys

and representing them in the form of maps. As a branch of knowledge, surveying and mapping has been systematically pursued since antiquity. At the entrance to the exhibition we show the earth as seen from space, together with a modern topographical map of Bavaria, measuring 2.5 x 5 m, and the first known map of Bavaria, produced by Philipp Apian in 1568. The various methods of measurement used in geodesy are dealt with in the next section. The measurement of lengths, heights, and angles are described, as is

△ Globe by Martin Behaim, 1492
△ Topographical map of Bavaria

for the land register.
The final part of the exhibition is devoted to cartography, starting with historic maps and globes and ending with editions of modern maps.
A relief model and map of Mount Everest illustrate how topographic features can be represented on a map.
Various types of map projection and the development of mapmaking from woodcuts to digital computer-generated maps are illustrated. *ms*

Computing is still a very young science. It deals with the systematic processing of information and operates with abstract concepts and relationships. The basic tool used in

dividers and slide rules. Before the advent of computers, the largest mathematical instruments were mechanical analog integrators. The large machines in the Department of Marine Navigation are also

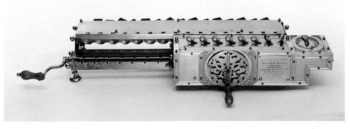

computer science is the computer itself. It had many predecessors, including various historical mathematical instruments and calculating machines. They all serve the same basic purpose, however: that of processing existing data in order to gain new information. Many of the ideas used by these forerunners may be seen at work in modern computers and form an integral part of recent data processing methods.

The two fundamental principles of analog and digital computation are distinguished by red and blue descriptions respectively.

Analog computation originated from the measurement of lengths and angles. Not only compasses and protractors, but also sundials and astrolabes make use of this principle. The most common instruments for analog computation include proportional

△ Leibniz calculator, about 1700
▽ Instantaneous planimeter, 1906

analog calculators and were used for predicting tides. For many years, electronic analog computers were indispensable in engineering. The glass cases by the windows contain numerous planimeters, integrators and integraphs, and two mechanical analyzers. Other mechanical integration machines include a Conzen OTT journey-time calculator, and three plotting boards belonging to the IPM OTT system.

Electronic analog computing is represented by two Telefunken machines.

Digital computation techniques are illustrated by various types of abacus, a calculating cloth, and Napier's 'bones'.

The distance travelled between the early calculating machines and modern industrial production of computers is illustrated by reconstructions of calculators built by Wilhelm Schickard (1623), Blaise Pascal (1642) Gottfried Wilhelm Leibniz (about 1700), and original machines constructed by Antonius Braun in about 1735 and Johann Christoph Schuster in 1792 and 1820.

Cipher machines are also digital. The best-known types are displayed along with explanations of basic cryptological principles.

Some ingeniously programmed clocks and musical automata are evidence that the control of automatic processes as used in a modern computer has a long history. Several machines controlled by a punch-card system are all in working order.

The world's first fully operational computer was built by Konrad Zuse in 1941. Known as the Z3, it was destroyed in the Second World War. An exact reconstruction of this machine demonstrates the basic functions of the computer. Other early computers built by Zuse are also displayed. It was only in the mid-1950s that computers began to be produced in large numbers. Up to that time, they were unique pieces of equipment, such as the PERM built by the Technische Hochschule in Munich or the G1 constructed by the Max Planck Institute in Göttingen. The first computers to be mass-produced in Germany and to become readily available were the PERM (1956), IBM 650 (1955), Siemens 2002 (1960), Telefunken TR4 (1962), and IBM 360-20 (1967).

Machines such as the Nixdorf FAC 820/15 (1971) represent the special group of office computers.

The central processing unit of a Cray 1 (1983) represents the high-performance computers. Pocket calculators, desk calculators and personal computers complete this broad spectrum of automation technology. *hp*

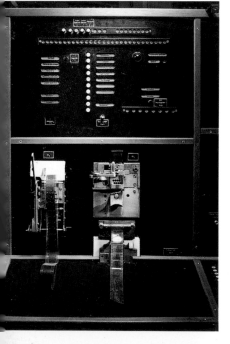

◁ Zuse Z4 computer, 1945
▷ Univac I, 1956
▷ Braun & Vayringe calculator, about 1735
▷ IPM OTT integrator, 1944
▷ Cray 1 computer, 1983

method of operation, which may be either bipolar or field-effect, and their functions, such as storage or logic components. Analog-digital converters, sensors and actuators, as well as circuit modules, complete this array of microelectronic components. Microelectronics are used in industrial equipment and plant, and also have important medical and domestic applications. Cardiac pacemakers, chip cards, robots, and movement sensors are just a few examples. The final section of the exhibition is dedicated to one of the most important applications of microelectronics: computers. The interaction of hardware and software solutions is demonstrated by a number of different computer systems, including text processing, speech recognition, and image analysis. *ob*

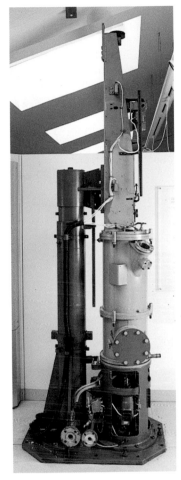

The field of telecommunications covers all the techniques and methods of exchanging and distributing messages over any required distance. A transmitter at one end encodes units of information, converts them to electrical or optical signals, and transmits them to a receiver at the other end which converts the signals back to their original form. When we make a

just after the French revolution, to computer-supported multifunctional telecommunications systems. An illuminated panel illustrates the journey and the processes a message undergoes from the sender to recipient. These include the conversion and encoding of the signals, their transmission by cable or radio, switching, and decoding and reconversion. The exhibition is designed around these

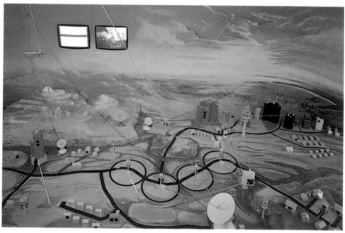

local telephone call which relies on an entirely analog process, the conversion of the sound waves produced by the voice is effected with the aid of a microphone, their transmission is along copper wires, and their reconversion takes place in the loudspeaker of the earpiece. Human speech acts as a code. An exchange ensures that communication is established with the desired partner. Six displays provide a short history of telecommunications, from the ancient use of beacons and the mechanical optical telegraphs introduced

△ Telecommunications environment
▷ Replica of the telephone built by A.G.Bell in 1876
▷ Mechanical optical telegraphic station, about 1800
▷ Manual telephone exchange, 1905

subjects, each of which is explored chronologically. Videos and interactive information systems offer more detailed explanations. In the gallery, there are terminals of various kinds. Equipment used for the transmission of texts includes the earliest surviving electric telegraph, built by Soemmerring in 1811,

a Morse code device, a telex terminal, and a personal computer. The history of the telephone is also traced and begins with apparatus built by Philipp Reis in 1861 and Alexander Graham Bell in 1876. Equipment combining several functions, such as the videophone and multimedia terminal, marks the end of this section. Grouped around the gallery

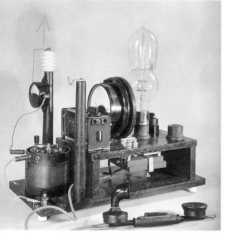

are several devices needed to establish communication. Telephone cables and broadband cables using copper wires and glass fibres illustrate some of the properties and applications of the different signal carriers.

Another means of transmission is by radio waves. A reconstruction of an experiment carried out in 1887 by Heinrich Hertz demonstrates the properties of electromagnetic waves in free space. Several radio transmitters are evidence of the widespread use of wireless telegraphy. The introduction of circuits using valves, in 1913, made it technically and economically possible to develop radio telephony and broadcasting systems. Further developments led to satellite communications and mobile radio services.

Radio and television broadcasting have a section to themselves. In radio, the sound quality improved markedly when the valve begun to replace the crystal detector in receivers, and VHF carriers gradually superseded long-wave carriers.

In the early days of television, pictures were scanned and reproduced mechanically, relying on the 'Nipkow disk'. Important technical breakthroughs led to the development of fully electronic television receivers and colour television. The introduction of semiconductor components and improved recording techniques saw the rise of the consumer electronics industry, which has traditionally availed itself of significant inventions such as the Edison drum, magnetic tape, the compact disc and video.

The exchange of information in the field of telecommunications takes place not only between people but between machines. Remote control engineering deals with the monitoring and operation of equipment such as air conditioning plants or power networks. Its history may be traced back to the early fire alarm systems which were developed in the 1850s, around the same time as the electric telegraph.

In the next section, the underlying principles of the processes taking place in transmitters, along the transmission path, and in receivers are examined. Signal modulation, analog-digital conversion, encoding, and multiplexing are all explained. The final part of the exhibition examines switching technology and communications networks. Beginning with public and private telephone exchanges, and culminating in the integrated-services digital network (ISDN), developments are described which illustrate the increasing fusion of all previous communication technologies into a global telecommunications system. *ob*

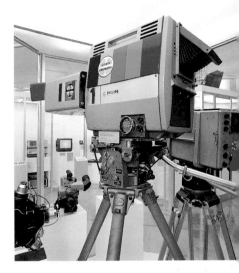

◁ Radio transmitter with Lieben tube,
  A. Meissner, 1913

△ Colour television camera, 1967

▽ Digital private communication system, 1989

A new era in the history of mankind began over 10 000 years ago. Towards the end of the Stone Age, man began to farm in a systematic way, discovering how to grow crops and domesticate animals. These advances in ensuring a regular food supply were linked to the establishment of

△ Windmill, 1866 (behind the museum)
△ A view of the exhibition

settlements and the invention of writing and mathematics. When the crops failed, however, ensuing starvation led to mass migration. Cultivating the soil was the most important development. Digging sticks, picks and hoes are among the oldest tools made by man. In medieval times, the heavy wheeled plough was the most common form of implement used to till the soil. Decisive increases in productivity were achieved with the advent of agricultural machinery which did not just depend on muscle power. Steam ploughs and motor-driven ploughs were restricted to a few large estates and cooperatives. Advances in the motorisation of farm machinery are due to the tractor. In use since the First World War, it has become the universal workhorse on the farm. Examples of sowing machines, and harvesting tools and machinery trace the development from the sickle to the combine harvester and document in an impressive way the dramatic pace of technological change.

Milk is a highly nutritious but perishable foodstuff and must be treated in some way if it is not meant for immediate consumption. For centuries, Alpine dairy farming was carried out exclusively by hand. Butter was made by agitating cream with a churn staff or churning it by hand, keeping it in constant motion until droplets of butterfat began to form lumps. Whereas butter-making is a purely physical process, cheese-making depends on chemical reactions. The first important step is to add rennet (an enzyme from a calf's stomach) and acidulating cultures in order to curdle the milk. The milk coagulates in a vat, and the curds, which subsequently clot and consist largely of casein, are separated from the whey. The process of skimming changed radically when centrifuges were introduced between 1875 and 1888. Centrifugal force rapidly separates the cream from the skimmed milk, which has a higher specific gravity. This revolutionary invention was immediately adopted by the dairy industry.

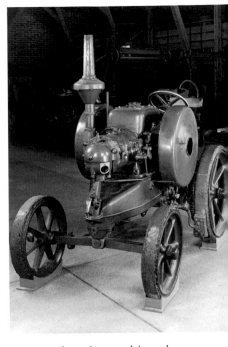

Cereals have been cultivated since Antiquity. The laborious task of grinding them is just as old. Simple, transportable stone slabs, querns and mortars have been in use for thousands of years. Rotary mills were only developed in the last few centuries BC. With the advent of watermills and windmills, which harnessed new types of motive power, milling rapidly developed into an occupation in its own right and acted as a model of technological progress right up to the industrial revolution. About 100 years ago, yields in white flour production increased as steel and porcelain rollers begun to replace the sets of millstones.

△ Lanz Bulldog, 1924
◁ Grinding corn

BEER was invented more or less by accident as a byproduct of bread-making. Sumerian documents dating from 4000 BC describe the close connection between the production of bread and beer from grain. The quantity of water used and the

SUGAR was extracted from sugar cane for many centuries. After cuttings had been introduced to the New World by Christopher Columbus in 1493, large areas of Central America and the Caribbean were turned over to its culti-

△ West Indies sugar works, about 1700

spontaneous fermentation brought about by the use of wild yeasts determined the end product. At the time, 'liquid bread' was a nutritious brew with only a very low alcohol content. Today's brewing methods are based on the work of the Frenchman Louis Pasteur, who recognized the role of micro-organisms in fermentation, the Dane Emil C. Hansen, who developed the cultivation of pure strains of yeast, and the German Carl von Linde, who designed and built refrigeration equipment. Control of the fermentation process made it possible to brew beer throughout the year.

vation. Sugar from the colonies was sold on the volatile European markets as fast as it could be produced. The gradual end of slavery on the plantations was not the result of an enlightened moral stance on the part of their owners, but came about due to the introduction of sugar beet in Europe. In 1747, the chemist Sigismund Marggraf had discovered that beet also contained the sweet tasting substance which was in such demand. It was left to Franz Carl Achard to breed the variety of sugar beet used for beet sugar refining, which began in 1802. As the 19th century progressed, this luxury foodstuff soon became part of our staple diet. *as*

The question of whether time really exists and what it actually may be, has still not been answered with any degree of certainty. Time does not seem to pose a problem for us in everyday life. Nor does it appear to hinder sporting activities or stand in the way of technological and scientific progress. With very few exceptions, the measurement of time would seem to be a simple matter, a clock or watch performing the task with ease. Difficulties only arise when we reflect more deeply on the nature of time. Down through the ages, an incredible variety of clocks has been produced and can hardly be dismissed as unimportant. The different principles on which they operated and the varied aspects of their design changed and developed over the centuries. The sundial, for example, marks the hours according to the apparent movement of the sun across the sky. Hourglasses and water clocks, on the other hand, measure the flow of time, as a material is emptied from a vessel. The reduction of a material is also

▷ Dial, 1592
▽ Turret clock, 1721

discernable in burning candles or oil lamps, which were also used as timekeepers. Mechanical and electrical clocks use discrete physical processes to indicate the time.

Numerous miniature sundials illustrate various methods of dividing up the day. In the courtyard of the Deutsches Museum, a sundial let into the flagstones uses the visitor's shadow to show local solar time. Several hourglasses and two Egyptian water clocks complete this section.

The range of mechanical timepieces extends from massive turret clocks to tiny wristwatches. Quartz watches were introduced in the 1930s and led to further improvements in accuracy. At last it was possible to measure precisely irregularities in the earth's rotation. Only a few watches restrict themselves to their original

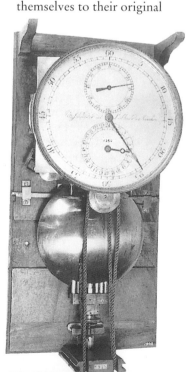

△ Black Forest wall clock, 17th century
◁ Precision regulator, 19th century

purpose of providing the wearer with the time of day. Perhaps they remind us of the transitoriness of human existence. Watches also have the welcome, incidental effect of indicating the owner's position in society. A watch was almost always a status symbol, an expensive adornment blending beauty and function. *hp*

Weighing and measuring are essential for every type of economic activity. There is hardly any field of human life in which weights and measures do not play an important role. Before any measurements can be carried out, however, a unit of measurement must first be defined. In the earliest international system of measurement, in order to put an end to this confusion. This Système International d'Unités (SI) was to use units of 'natural' measurement such as the ten-millionth part of a 'meridian', the distance around the earth from pole to pole. The metric system was based on these principles, but it

△ Scales and weighing platform

advanced civilizations, lengths, volumes, and masses were expressed in units. Their validity, however, was limited to specific periods and certain regions. During the 17th and 18th centuries, there was still an abundance of values for yard, foot and pound, which varied slightly from place to place. This was a source of great inconvenience, especially with the growth of regional trade.

In 1790, the French National Assembly proposed a uniform took another 200 years before the SI units were recognised as an international standard. Today, many units of measurement are derived from natural constants. A standard unit of 1 metre, for example, is defined as the distance travelled by light in a vacuum in one 299 792 458th of a second. The exhibition traces the historical development of units of length, volume and mass. *ab*

The Astronomy section is housed on the third, fourth, and fifth floors, and divided into ten distinct sections. On the third floor, the visitor can gain an understanding of how the universe is structured. A large display contains several models of the broad band of fixed stars which surrounds our sun, and depicts the large structures of the cosmos.

The second section is devoted to the observation of the stars in the sky. The different types of celestial bodies and their motion are described as well as the development of various cosmological traditions throughout history.

Well into the 19th century, the main objective of astronomy was to measure the positions of heavenly bodies as accurately as possible. Exhibits include measuring instruments from several centuries (in the main showcase), a mural quadrant from 1768 (mounted on the wall), and a large heliometer from 1889 (in the middle of the room). Around the middle of the 19th century, the quantity and quality of light produced by the stars formed the basis of the emerging discipline of astrophysics. Since then, analysis of the radiation emitted by stars has allowed information to be gathered about their chemical composition and motion. Special stars of variable brightness can be used to measure inter-stellar distances. Of special importance are the three-prism spectrometer

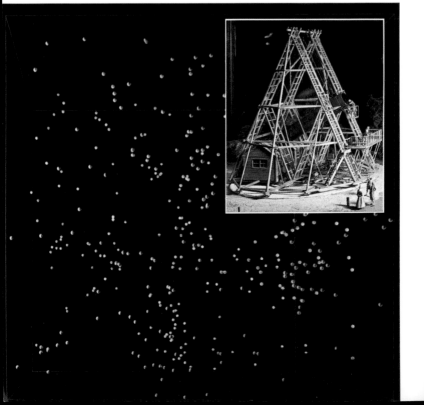

built in 1902 and a number of
photometers (in the main
showcase). Various demon-
strations explain how
brightness is measured, the
Doppler effect, and different
types of spectra and how they
can be analysed.

Every star has its own life
cycle. It is born, exists for millions and millions of years,
and then dies. The night sky
contains stars of all ages. An
illuminated demonstration
using the Hertzsprung-Russell
diagram illustrates the evolu-
tion of stars. Using an original

Wolter telescope, built in 1977,
the principles of gathering
stellar X-ray emissions and

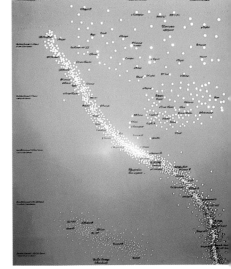

△ Astronomical instruments
◁ Large structure of the universe
◁ Wilhelm Herschel's telescope,
   18th century
▷ Hertzsprung-Russell diagram

making visible this form of radiation are explained.

The final section on the third floor is dedicated to galaxies. Some of these vast conglomerations of stars are also known as spiral nebulae. By measuring the distances between galaxies, it is possible to gain a rough idea of the extent of the visible universe. A segment of the reflector from a sub-millimetre telescope indicates the size of instrument needed to receive light from distant galaxies. In the gallery, the development is traced of astronomical instru-

ments used to detect the various types of electro-magnetic radiation, including visible light, ultra-violet rays, infra-red rays, radio waves, X-rays and gamma rays. A large display detailing the wavelengths involved indicates how far these rays can penetrate the earth's atmosphere. The telescope built by Simon Marius in 1613 and the first 'active' telescope mirror, dating from 1986, deserve particular attention.

The Amateur Astronomy exhibition on the fourth floor illustrates how astronomy can be pursued as a hobby, describes the equipment needed, and the results that can be achieved. Examples of typical amateur telescopes and a large star finder wheel or 'planisphere' are displayed. This can be adjusted to display the night sky exactly as it appeared on a certain date and at a specific time. In the adjacent stairwell, a solar telescope tracks the sun on clear days and, via a series of mirrors on the fifth floor, projects a 'live' solar spectrum with the characteristic dark Fraunhofer lines. In a glass showcase, there is a model of our sun, explaining its characteristics and structure. Demonstrations of a solar

△ Wolter telescope, built in the 1970s and 1980s

◁ Stonehenge: Astronomy in the Stone Age

▷ Segment of a radio telescope, about 1990

▷ The planet Neptune

▷ Meteorite

▷ Solar spectrum

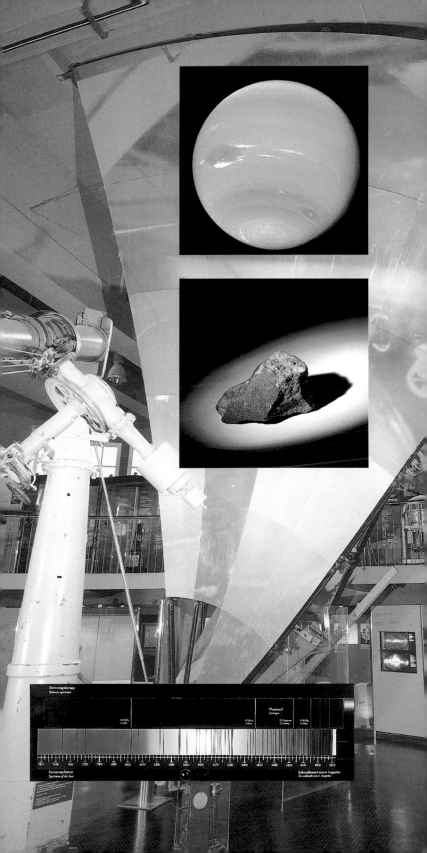

eclipse are held regularly. The sun is the central object of our solar system. In elliptical orbits around the sun are the earth, eight other planets – some of them with moons – asteroids, meteorites, and comets. The characteristic motion of the planets is explained by means of a gravity well. A model on the ceiling demonstrates how the loops in their orbits came about. Historic planetaria, some genuine meteorites, models demonstrating the kinematics of the solar system, and a set of 'planetary scales' are among the most important exhibits. The final part of the exhibition concerns the

history of mankind's conception of the universe, various cosmological systems and traditions, including the question of how life began on earth, and the search for extraterrestrial forms of life. Other interesting exhibits include a whirlpool designed to represent the accretion disk of a black hole, the original apparatus with which cosmic background radiation was discovered in 1965, and a fragment of the Allende meteorite, which was found to contain amino acids – the building blocks of all living organisms. Visitors can test their astronomical knowledge by taking part in a computer quiz.

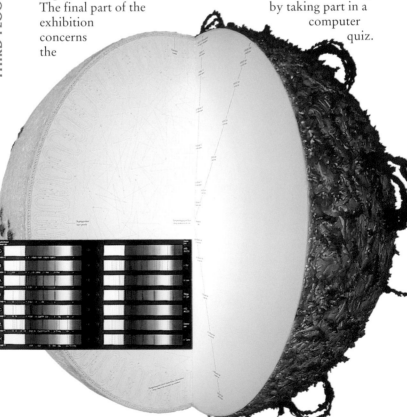

The observatory consists of two domes from which the skies over Munich can be observed. The western dome is open daily from 10.30 to 11.30. It is equipped with a 30 cm refractor built by Carl Zeiss, Jena. This lens telescope allows the sun, moon, several planets, and the brightest fixed stars to be observed – even by day. There are guided tours of the eastern dome at 20.00 and 21.00 every Saturday evening from October to the end of March. The eastern dome is equipped with a mirror telescope, the 40 cm reflector built by Goerz, Berlin. Other astronomical

exhibits include an astronomical clock on the inner wall of the clock tower, and the *Würzburg Riese*, a giant radio telescope behind the museum. Finally, there is an enjoyable 'interplanetary walk' covering the 4.6 km to Munich's zoo at Hellabrunn. The planets are marked along the way, the distances between them measured out in the same proportion as in our own solar system.

△ Observatory
◁ Cross-section through the sun
◁ Spectral analysis

The heart of the planetarium on the sixth floor of the Deutsches Museum is a computer controlled Zeiss projector. An artificially produced but realistic image of the firmaments is projected onto the inner surface of a 15 metre dome. Visitors can see the sun, moon, the planets Mercury, Venus, Mars, Jupiter and Saturn, and about 5000 stars visible to the naked eye. The apparent motion of the stars is speeded up and the appearance of the night sky demonstrated at various times of the year and from different points on the earth. Special admission tickets are on sale on the ground floor. *gh*

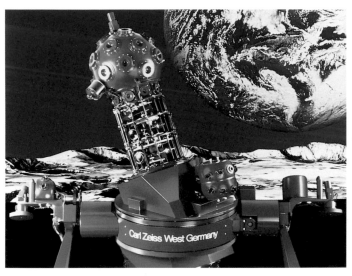

△ Zeiss Planetarium, designed in the 1980s

▽ Amateur radio station, DL Ø DM

Amateur radio enthusiasts pursue their interest in global communications for technical as well as social reasons. The field covers the sending of Morse code messages and speech as well as television broadcasting and data transmission on specially allocated frequencies. Home-made and commercially available equipment illustrate the history of amateur radio from the spark transmitter to satellite communications. There are daily demonstrations in the museum's own amateur radio station, callsign DL Ø DM. *ob*

ADDITIONAL DEPARTMENTS AND SERVICES OF THE DEUTSCHES MUSEUM

The Deutsches Museum Research Institute for the History of Science and Technology operates in conjunction with the *Institute of the History of Science of the Ludwig Maximilian University* and the *Central Institute of the History of Technology of the Munich Technical University.* All three are housed in the Deutsches Museum. A regular series of lectures and colloquia is announced in the programme of events. Tel. 2179-280.

The *Archive, Special Collections,* and *Documentation Department* on the third floor of the library building hold large collections on the history of science and technology, including bequests, manuscripts, papers, certificates, technical drawings, and an aerospace archive. Tel. 2179-220.

The *Photographic Service Department* holds about 40 000 negatives. Copies can be ordered or new photographs commissioned. Tel. 2179-231.

The *Library* of the Deutsches Museum specializes in the history of science and technology. It holds 750 000 books and 4300 periodicals, of which 1700 are current publications. As it is purely a reference library, every book is available at any time.

The *Libri Rari* collection is a small museum on its own, with about 5000 valuable historical works. Tel. 2179-224.

The *Reserve Collection* of the Deutsches Museum contains many examples of historic apparatus, machines, instruments, models, and prototypes, but is open only to specialists, who should apply at least two weeks in advance. Tel. 2179-459.

The *Kerschensteiner College* offers one-week courses on the history of science and technology for students, teachers, instructors, and scientists from around the world. The courses are usually organized in cooperation with other institutions, in line with individual wishes. Tel. 2179-243.

The *Museum Shop* in the Deutsches Museum sells guide books, catalogues, and current publications, as well as a wide selection of scientific literature and publications on the history of science and technology, published in both German and English. Scientific instruments, models, construction kits, experiments, toys such as kites, and card and wooden models in kit form may also be purchased along with unusual and simple presents. Tel. 299931.

A complete *Catalogue of Deutsches Museum Publications* can be obtained in the Museum Shop or from the Publications Department. Tel. 2179-247.

When dialling any of the above Munich telephone numbers from outside the city, but within Germany, use the code 089.

Published by the Deutsches Museum
Museumsinsel 1, D-80538 München, Germany
Tel. (089) 2179-1

Editing, production, layout:
Graham Lack, Birgit Heilbronner, Rolf Gutmann
Translation: Graham Lack, Hugh Casement

Photographs: Hans-Joachim Becker, Susanne Hochmuth,
Reinhard Krause, Constanze Danner
Plans: Jank und Frenzel
Cover design: Andreas Linke, Christian Hölzl
Authors: Karl Allwang (*ka*), Margareta Benz-Zauner (*mb*),
Oskar Blumtritt (*ob*), Alto Brachner (*ab*), Jobst Broelmann (*jb*),
Dirk Bühler (*db*), Gerhard Filchner (*gf*), Klaus Freymann (*kf*),
Winfrid Glocker (*wg*), Bettina Gundler (*bg*), Birte Hantke (*bh*),
Gerhard Hartl (*gh*), Friedrich Heilbronner (*fh*), Werner Heinzerling (*wh*),
Hubert Henkel (*hhe*), Sylvia Hladky (*sh*), Hans Holzer (*hho*),
Cornelia Kemp (*ck*), Günter Knerr (*gk*), Matthias Knopp (*mk*),
Wilhelm Kretzler (*wk*), Hartmut Petzold (*hp*), Günther Probeck (*gp*),
Ernst Rödl (*er*), Ludwig Schletzbaum (*ls*), Max Seeberger (*ms*),
Hans Straßl (*hs*), Andrea Stützle (*as*), Horst Tietzel (*ht*)
(all on the staff at the Deutsches Museum)
Introductory texts: Ralf Bülow

*With 216 illustrations, mostly in colour,
and 5 floor plans*

ISBN 3-924183-41-4
© 1997 Deutsches Museum
Reproduction of the illustrations:
Repro-Knopp, Inning/Ammersee
Type Setting: Wolfgang Lehner, München
Printing: Appl, Wemding
Paper: BVS woodfree, matt-coated repro quality,
135 g/m², by Papierfabrik Scheufelen, 73252 Lenningen
The paper is made of cellulose, bleached without chlorine,
and is non-ageing.
Binding: Sellier, Freising
Printed in Germany